The
BIG
and
BRILLIANT
Activity Book

The
BIG
and
BRILLIANT
Activity Book

ANGELA WILKES
SUSAN ADAMS

A Dorling Kindersley Book

CONTENTS

GLOBAL GAMES

RAINY-DAY ACTIVITIES

INTRODUCTION

This book is packed full of hundreds of ideas and instructions about brilliant things to do and make. As you complete the activities, you will learn invaluable basic skills in arts and crafts, sewing, cooking, and gardening. Once you have mastered these skills, you can be creative and invent new activities and projects of your own. Adapt and combine the ideas that you see in this book and, most of all, have lots of fun!

Things to collect

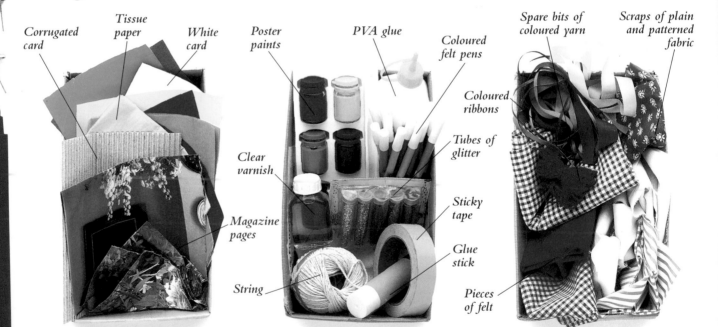

Corrugated card

Tissue paper

White card

Poster paints

PVA glue

Coloured felt pens

Spare bits of coloured yarn

Scraps of plain and patterned fabric

Clear varnish

Coloured ribbons

Tubes of glitter

Magazine pages

Sticky tape

String

Glue stick

Pieces of felt

Brilliant bits and bobs

Try recycling all your old junk to make some wonderful new things. Look at the materials on this page and then see what you can find around your home – it's amazing what you can do with bottle tops, buttons, and boxes! Save different types of paper, card, and scraps of fabric and ribbons. You will also need glue, paint, and sticky tape for many activities. Store all your bits and pieces carefully in boxes, folders, or pots so that they don't get damaged.

Seeing stars

Before you start a project, check how long it will take to complete! Use the star key at the top of each page to find out how long the most difficult project on each page takes.

⭐ **One star**
An hour or less

⭐⭐ **Two stars**
A whole afternoon

⭐⭐⭐ **Three stars**
A day or more

Warning symbols

Always read the instructions very carefully and look out for the red warning signs below. Whenever you see one, you will need to ask an adult to help you.

The oven glove symbol
When you see this symbol in a cooking project, put on oven gloves and ask an adult to help you.

The warning symbol
You will see this sign when sharp tools are used. Always ask an adult to help you.

Lots of coloured sequins

Pins

Beads in lots of different shapes and colours

Plastic bottle tops

Small boxes

Twigs and pieces of wood

Feathers

Sticker stars

Paperclips

Lentils and seeds

Small, brightly coloured buttons

Paper plates

Small cardboard tubes

Egg box

Fir and pine cones

Seashells

Straw and hessian

Interesting leaves

Getting started and finishing up

Look through the book and see which activities appeal to you. Always tell an adult what you want to do so that they can help you plan your projects and complete some of the more difficult stages. For activities that involve painting, you may want to put on overalls or old clothes and spread out newspapers before you start. When you have finished, clean up any mess you have made and carefully put away all your materials ready for next time.

MAKING PICTURES

One of the best ways to spend a rainy day is to make pictures. You don't even have to be good at drawing, as you can produce brilliant mosaics and collages from paper, seeds, pasta, magazine photographs, scraps of fabric, and glue. Below, you can see how to make the different sorts of pictures. Turn the page to see the finished works of art and to find out how to frame them.

EQUIPMENT

Sticky tape

Ruler

Thick paintbrush

Thin paintbrush

Craft knife★

Spatula

Jar of water

Felt pen

Cotton buds

Scissors

You will need

PVA glue

Scraps of fabric

Pages torn out of old magazines

Coloured paper

Different types of white card and paper

Dried beans, seeds, and pasta

Smooth stones and pebbles

Poster paints

Clear varnish

Glue stick

Corrugated cardboard

Mosaic picture

1 Mosaics look best if you keep the shape or pattern simple. Start by drawing the outline of your picture on a piece of white card.

2 Choose the colours you want to use in your picture. Find these colours in magazines and tear the magazine pages into small squares.

3 Use glue to stick down the coloured squares. Start with the background and work in rows from the top downwards.

Paper or fabric pictures

1 Choose a piece of paper or fabric for the background, then cut it out and stick it down. Then glue strips of paper or fabric around the border.

2 Tear out paper shapes for the main image in the picture. Arrange them on the background until you are happy with the design. Glue it down.

3 Add the details to your pictures with smaller pieces of paper. Arrange the pieces on the picture before you glue them in position.

Painted pebbles

1 Choose smooth pebbles or stones. Wash them and let them dry. Next paint the pebbles all over with a thick coat of white paint and let it dry.

2 Now, paint a picture on each stone. Paint the larger areas of colour first and let them dry before painting the smaller details, with a thin brush, on top.

3 When the paint has dried, brush each pebble with clear varnish and let it dry. This helps to stop paint chipping off the stone.

Seed collage

1 Sort out lots of different coloured seeds, dried beans, and pasta. Draw an outline of your picture on a piece of white card.

2 Spread glue on part of the picture and carefully sprinkle some beans or seeds on top. Push them into place with the hard end of your paintbrush.

3 Continue sticking on seeds until the picture is finished. Add small details with lines of beans or seeds, or by breaking off small pieces of pasta.

PICTURES ON DISPLAY

Coral fish mosaic

Making a frame

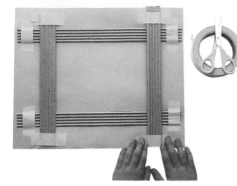

1 Cut four long strips of corrugated card each about 3 cm wide. Tape them together, on some card, to fit the size of picture you are framing.

2 Ask an adult to score the edges of the card strips diagonally, as shown. Cut the strips along the score lines. Then peel off the sticky tape.

3 Turn the card over and tape the edges together. Paint and varnish the front of the frame, then tape the picture to the back of the frame.

Painted corrugated card frame

On display

Here is a gallery of all the different sorts of pictures you can make. The instructions on the left show you how to make frames for your pictures, or you could mount them on a sheet of coloured paper or card, instead.

Why not make frames for your paintings, too?

Seaside painting

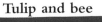

Fabric collage cow

Fabric fun
Make a collection of different sorts of fabric with interesting textures colours and patterns for your collages.

Marmalade cat

Tulip and bee

Torn paper pictures
These torn paper pictures are simple to make, and they look stunning, too. Try making cards and gift tags in the same way.

Painted pebbles and shells
These pebbles have a sea-side theme. The shapes of your pebbles may suggest other ideas. The stones make fun paperweights.

Duck in the snow

Boat at sea

Beach crab

Shoal of fish

Sun and sea

Orange paper mount

Seed street collage

PAINTED POTS

Why not brighten up your house plants by painting some flowerpots to put them in? You can make plain-coloured pots, add stripes and checks, or paint on some flowers. For the best effects, keep the paint quite thick and the patterns simple. Painted pots make attractive and useful presents, too.

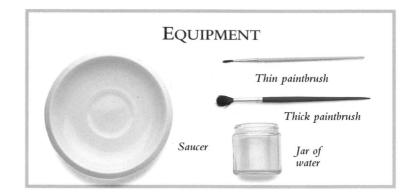

EQUIPMENT

Thin paintbrush

Thick paintbrush

Saucer

Jar of water

You will need

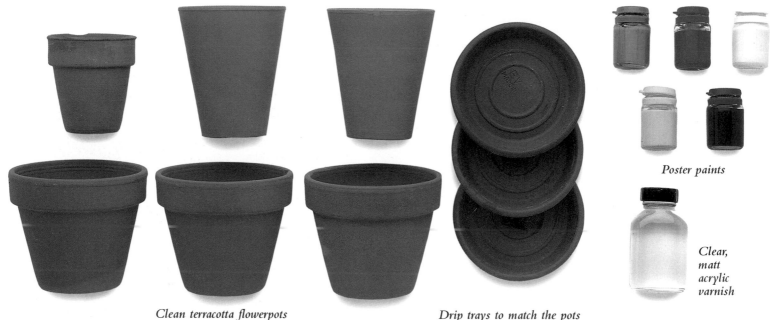

Clean terracotta flowerpots

Drip trays to match the pots

Poster paints

Clear, matt acrylic varnish

What to do

1 First mix the colours you want on a saucer. Use a thick brush to paint large areas of one colour, and a fine brush for patterns, like these.

2 To make patterns, paint pots in one colour and leave them to dry. Then paint stripes or checks in other colours on top of the first colour.

3 When the paint has dried, brush on a coat of clear varnish. This will make the pots waterproof and stop the paint running.

You can paint pots of all shapes and sizes. This little pot has cress growing in it.

Blue and yellow design

Plenty of pots

Here is a selection of painted pots and some of the ways you can use them, from growing houseplants and fragrant kitchen herbs, to making perfect candle holders, and a colourful desk tidy. If your pot has a drip tray, try painting it with a matching design.

Plain-coloured pot

This tiny pot makes a pretty candle holder.

Daisy design

Spotty pot design

Paint criss-cross lines for a tartan design.

Ivy

This is a herb called marjoram. Find out more about growing herbs on page 58.

Try painting the inside of the pot in a matching colour.

Stripy pot and matching drip tray

Pink tulip design

DOUGH MODELS

Salt dough is easy to make and can be modelled into all kinds of things. You can bake it in the oven so that it sets hard (ask an adult to help you), and then paint it bright colours. Here you can see how to make jazzy napkin rings, tiny coil pots, fabulous fishy key rings, and fun play-food badges.

EQUIPMENT

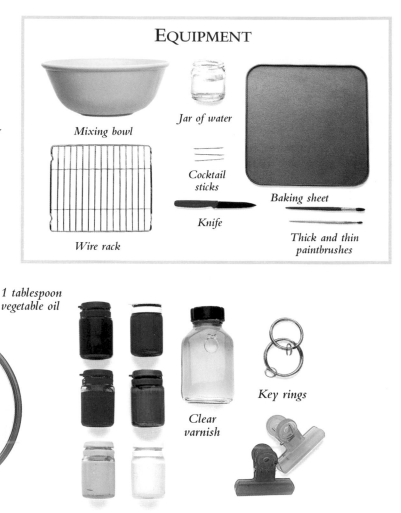

Mixing bowl

Jar of water

Cocktail sticks

Baking sheet

Knife

Wire rack

Thick and thin paintbrushes

You will need

200 ml water

1 tablespoon vegetable oil

300 g plain flour

300 g salt

Clear varnish

Key rings

Poster paints

Plastic bulldog clips

What to do

1 Set the oven to 180°C/350°F/Gas Mark 4. Mix the flour, salt, oil, and water into a soft dough in the bowl. Add more water if necessary.

2 Sprinkle some flour on the table Turn the dough on to the table and knead it with your hands, as shown, until it is smooth and stretchy.

3 Then, model the dough into the shapes you want. Stick pieces of dough together with a little water and use a cocktail stick to make small holes.

Fishy friends
You can use your models to make great presents, like fridge magnets, key rings and paperclips.

Fishy clip

4 Make a pot by coiling sausages of dough around on a circular base. Put all the dough shapes on a baking sheet and bake them for 20 minutes.

5 Let the dough shapes cool on a wire rack, then paint them in bright colours. When the paint has dried, coat them with clear varnish.

Glue a fish on to a small magnet.

Fridge magnet

Play cakes

Play meal

Play fruit

Jewel bright

Here are some of the many things you can make with salt dough. Once they are painted and varnished, they will last for ever. Try making salt dough jewellery, too.

Tie a fish to a key ring with ribbon.

Key ring

Play-food badges
Tape your mini plate on to a safety pin to make a colourful badge.

Paint your pots with colourful designs.

Mini coil pots
You can keep beads, jewellery, and other treasures in these pretty pots.

Make a personalised napkin ring for each member of your family.

Napkin rings
These colourful rings will brighten up any table. You could try making a bangle in the same way.

15

PAPER POTTERY

Papier mâché costs very little to make as it is made out of torn up newspaper. You can make the most amazing pottery with a few simple moulds. Here and over the page you can see how to create a golden treasure chest and bright plates and bowls for holding and displaying your treasures.

For the papier mâché

Old newspaper and white paper

PVA glue

You will need

For the treasure chest

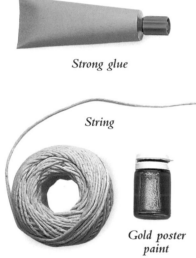

Strong glue

String

Gold poster paint

Corrugated card

Small, oval gemstones★

Glitter paint

Sticky tape

Large, round gemstones★

Box with a lid

Making the plate

1 Tear newspaper into long strips and squares about 2 cm across. Mix PVA glue with a little water in a bowl and soak the paper in it.

2 Using the plate as a mould, cover the back with plastic wrap, then with six layers of glued paper. Make sure all the pieces of paper overlap.

3 Tear up some strips of white paper, soak them in the glue, and cover the plate with them. Leave the papier mâché to dry for a day.

★*Available from large department stores or craft shops.*

EQUIPMENT

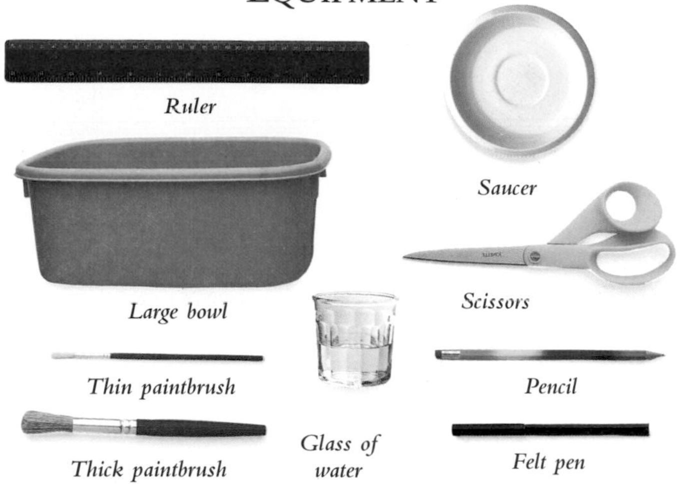

Ruler

Saucer

Large bowl

Scissors

Thin paintbrush

Pencil

Thick paintbrush

Glass of water

Felt pen

Gold and coloured tissue paper

For the plate and bowl

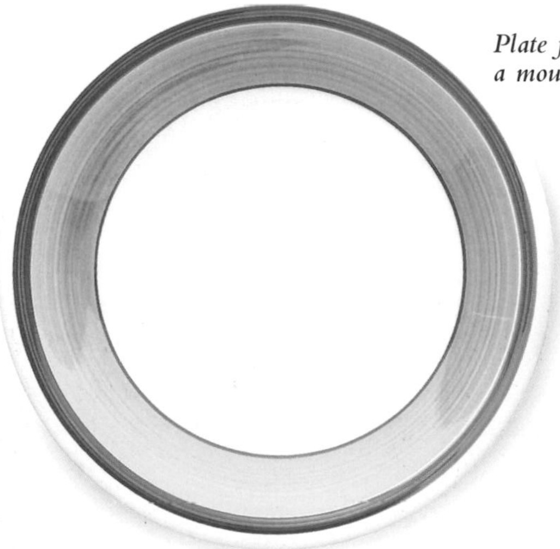

Plate for a mould

Poster paints

Large bowl for a mould

White card

Plastic wrap

Decorating the plate

Painting the bowl

4 Remove the mould. Cover the top of the paper plate with white paper soaked in glue. When it is dry, trim the edges of the plate.

Paste squares of coloured tissue paper on to the plate and gold tissue paper around the rim. Cover the bottom of the plate with gold tissue paper.

Make a bowl in the same way as the plate. Draw a pattern on the bowl, then paint it with poster paint. Paint the inside of the bowl gold.

TREASURE TROVE

Making the chest

1 Cut out a piece of white card the same width as the box lid but twice as long. Fold under two flaps and tape these to the top of the lid.

2 Trace round the hole at the side of the lid on to card twice. Add 1 cm all round and cut out. Snip the edges and tape to the sides of the lid.

3 Cut a circle and four stars out of corrugated card and glue string on top. Cut a strip of card with zigzag edges for each side of the box lid.

Glittering treasures

The finished paper pottery is light, but surprisingly strong. You could use the treasure chest to store interesting bits and pieces. The decorated papier mâché objects make great presents for family and friends.

Foil-covered chocolate coins

Red, blue, and green tissue paper

Patchwork plate

Squares of brightly coloured tissue paper are glued on to the plate to look like patchwork. You could try paler colours, or paint the plate instead.

This plate is edged with squares of gold tissue paper.

Elephant bowl

This bowl is painted with a bold design of elephants and stars. It is best to paint one colour at a time and let it dry before adding the next one, so the colours don't run. Try making up your own design.

4 Cover the box and lid with papier mâché★. When dry, glue the zigzag strips to the lid and cover them. Repeat with the card shapes.

5 Tear out lots of strips of white paper. Dip them in a mixture of PVA glue and water and paste them all over the box and lid.

6 When dry, paint the box and lid gold. Then carefully glue oval gemstones on the box and round ones to the shapes on the box lid.

Star shape made from card and string

Treasure chest
The chunky chest has an old medieval look. If you can't find gemstones like those shown here, make your own by covering balls of paper with coloured foil sweet wrappers.

Oval gemstone

Zigzag edging made from corrugated card

RAGGY DOLLS

Here and overleaf are some wonderful things to sew – teddies, little cats and bears, pretty hearts, a rag doll, and a rabbit. You can make all of them using leftover pieces of fabric you have at home. You will find the templates on pages 236 and 237, and help with easy sewing stitches on page 235.

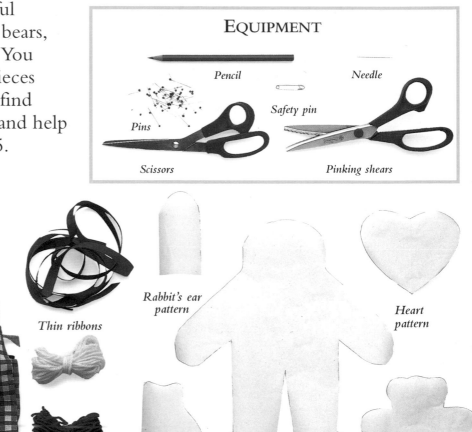

EQUIPMENT

Pencil

Needle

Safety pin

Pins

Scissors

Pinking shears

You will need

Kapok or other soft stuffing

Reels of thread

Pieces of calico and gingham or other scraps of fabric

Thin ribbons

White and red wool

Rabbit's ear pattern

Heart pattern

Cat pattern

Rabbit or doll pattern

Teddy pattern

(See pages 236 and 237 for all the templates)

Making the toys

1 Fold the fabric in half. Pin the pattern to the folded fabric and cut it out, as shown, to give you two pieces. Then unpin the pattern.

2 Lay the two pieces of fabric right sides together. Pin and then sew★ them together, leaving a gap 5 cm wide at the end of the seam.

3 Trim the seam, then turn the toy inside out. Use a pencil to push out any narrow points. Then push some stuffing into the toy.

Finishing the rabbit

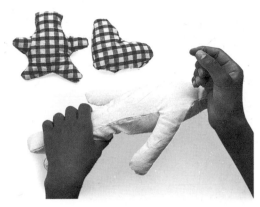

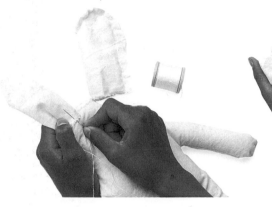

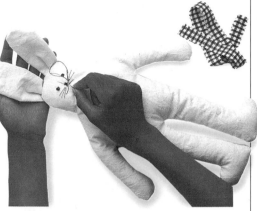

4 Use a pencil to push stuffing into any small corners. When the toy seems fat enough, sew up the gap in the seam, using overstitch.

1 Fold the rabbit ears in half and sew★ round the outer edges. Turn them inside out. Sew them to the top of the rabbit's head using overstitch.

2 Sew eyes, a nose, a mouth, and whiskers on the rabbit's face using backstitch. Cut a strip of fabric and tie it on like a bow tie.

Finishing the doll

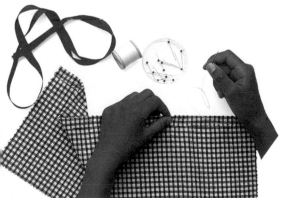

Long strands of red wool

White wool

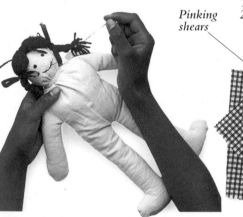

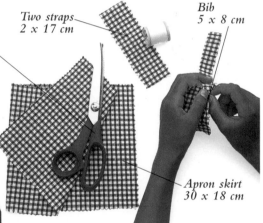

Two straps 2 x 17 cm

Pinking shears

Bib 5 x 8 cm

Apron skirt 30 x 18 cm

1 Tie white wool round the doll's neck. Sew red wool to her head for hair. Sew two ribbons to her face. Tie them in bows round her hair.

2 Plait the hair beneath the bows and tie each plait with red wool. Then sew two eyes and a mouth on to the doll's face, using backstitch.

3 Cut out the apron pieces with shears. Fold the straps in half and overstitch them to the bib. Put the bib on the doll so the straps cross at the back.

Trim off the ends of the ribbon.

Tie the apron round the doll.

4 Cut a 30 cm length of ribbon. Fold the top of the apron over by 1 cm and pin it down. Sew★ along the cut edge to make a casing.

5 Fasten a safety pin to one end of the ribbon and thread the ribbon though the casing. Then gather the skirt evenly along the ribbon.

DOLLS AND TEDDIES

Add bows and ribbons to your toys to give them a finishing touch. You can make them in matching fabrics as we have done here, or use any scraps you find at home. All of them would make good presents.

Dancing bears
Make three little bears. Tie bows round their necks and stitch them together at the paws. Then sew short ribbons at each end of the row of bears. These make an ideal decoration for a baby's pram or cot.

Red wool hair tied into plaits.

Embroidered face

Sew a red ribbon bow around each teddy's neck.

Blue ribbon bow

Gingham apron

Blue ribbon bow

Martha doll
Martha is made of white calico and has a checked apron, to give her an American prairies look.

Soft hearts cushion
Make four stuffed hearts in different fabrics that go well together. Sew them together to make a flower shape and stitch a bow in the centre.

Red stripy
fabric

Ribbons for tying
up the bears

Broad ribbon
loop for hanging
up the hearts

Embroidered
face and
whiskers

Gingham
bow tie

Red bow of
thin ribbon

White rabbit
The rabbit is made from the
same pattern as Martha
doll, only he has floppy
ears as well. Tie a
jaunty bow tie round
his neck. Make him
a posy of dried
flowers and sew
them on the
inside of
one paw.

Tie a red bow
around the
cat's neck to
give it a little
more shape.

Little cat
Make the little cat from simple checked
fabric and tie a bow round its neck.

Row of
hearts
Make four
stuffed hearts.
Sew a loop at
the top of a
broad ribbon,
then sew the
hearts beneath it.

23

ALL IN A POCKET

Here you can find out how to make a cook's apron, a gardener's apron, a tool kit, and an organiser. Copy the patterns at the bottom of the page using the measurements shown. Use running stitch★ to sew the aprons. Turn the page to see the final results.

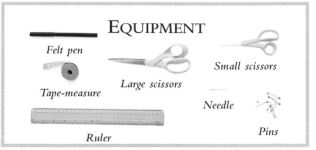

EQUIPMENT

Felt pen

Tape-measure

Large scissors

Small scissors

Needle

Pins

Ruler

You will need

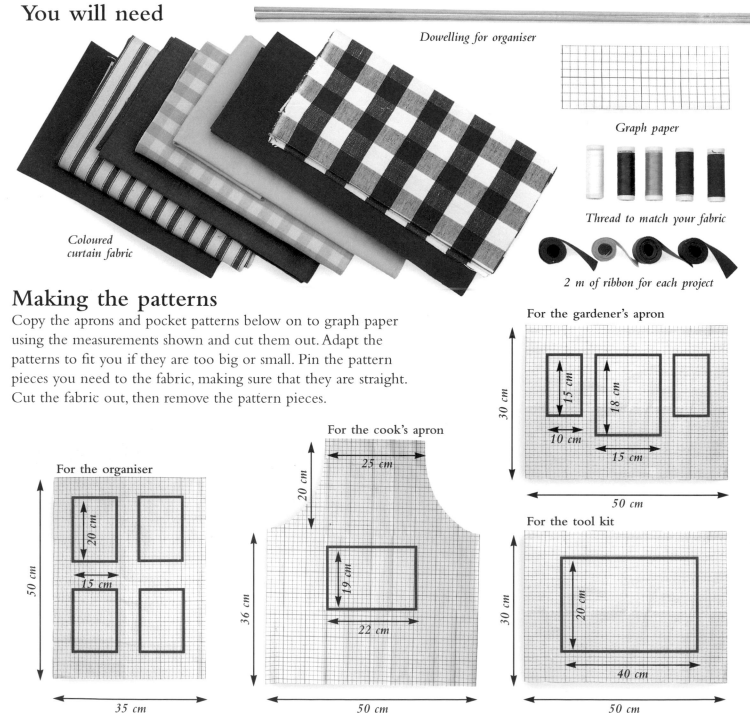

Dowelling for organiser

Graph paper

Coloured curtain fabric

Thread to match your fabric

2 m of ribbon for each project

Making the patterns

Copy the aprons and pocket patterns below on to graph paper using the measurements shown and cut them out. Adapt the patterns to fit you if they are too big or small. Pin the pattern pieces you need to the fabric, making sure that they are straight. Cut the fabric out, then remove the pattern pieces.

For the gardener's apron

15 cm
18 cm
30 cm
10 cm
15 cm
50 cm

For the cook's apron

25 cm
20 cm
19 cm
22 cm
36 cm
50 cm

For the organiser

20 cm
15 cm
50 cm
35 cm

For the tool kit

20 cm
30 cm
40 cm
50 cm

Find out how to sew a running stitch on page 235.

Making the cook's apron

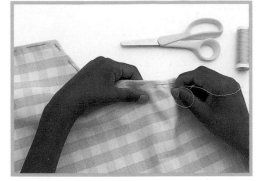 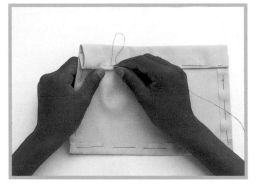 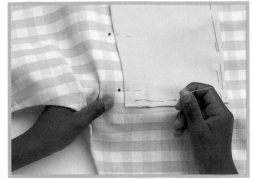

1 To make a neat hem, fold the apron material over 1 cm at the edge and fold it again. Tack★ the edge in place then sew it in running stitch.

2 Tack a 1 cm hem around the sides and bottom of the pocket. Tack and sew a hem 1.5 cm deep at the top edge of the pocket.

3 Pin the pocket to the centre of the apron. Tack the pocket in place then sew it in running stitch along the bottom and sides.

Making the organiser

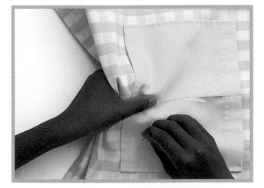 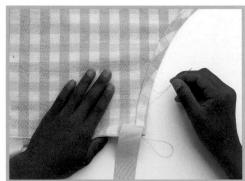 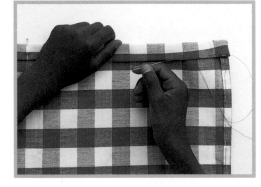

4 Tack a line across the middle of the pocket to divide it in two. Using the tacking as a guide, sew a straight line across the pocket.

5 Cut a ribbon 56 cm long for the apron top and two ribbons 50 cm long for each side. Fold over the ends and sew them to the apron back.

1 Tack and sew a 1 cm hem down the long sides of the fabric. Tack and sew a 2 cm hem at the top and bottom of the rectangle.

Making the tool kit

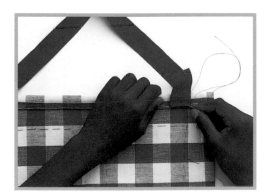 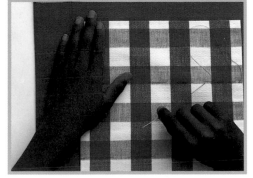 

2 Make the pockets as in step 2 above. Pin, tack, and sew them to the fabric. Cut a ribbon 40 cm long and sew it to the top of the organiser.

1 Sew the edges of the kit. Tack and sew on the pocket, as for the cook's apron. To divide up the pocket, sew two lines 10 cm from each side.

2 Cut four 50 cm lengths of ribbon. Sew two ribbons on the back of the top right corner and the other two to the bottom right corner.

★To tack, sew in big stitches using contrasting thread. Remove the tacking stitches when you have done the running stitch. 25

KITS AND APRONS
Making the gardener's apron

1 Hem the edges of the apron and make the pockets as for the cook's apron. Pin, tack, and sew the pockets to the apron 7 cm from the top edge.

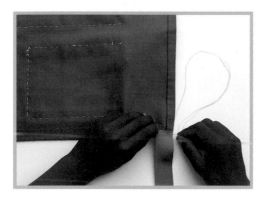

2 Cut two pieces of ribbon 50 cm long. Turn in the edges and sew one ribbon to each top edge of the apron, at the back of the fabric.

Finished products
Choose fabrics in bold colours or patterns for the kits and aprons. Checks and stripes look good with plain colours and are easy to sew as you can use them as guidelines for stitching.

Organiser
Hang the organiser on your bedroom wall or above a desk. Use it to hold all your pens and store other odds and ends.

Hang the organiser up by the ribbon loop.

To make the organiser hang correctly, insert the dowelling into the 2 cm hems at the top and bottom.

Individual pockets

Pocket in a contrasting colour to checked fabric

Gardener's apron
Tuck your gardening tools, gloves, and packets of seeds away in these practical pockets. Roll up the apron when you have finished using it.

Two smaller pockets at each side of a large pocket

Tool kit

Keep your work area tidy by putting your tools, screws, and nails together in the divided pockets of the tool kit. Roll the kit up, starting from the end without the ties. Fasten the kit by tying the four ties at the end around the kit.

Two ties sewn to one side at the top

Two ties sewn at the bottom of the kit

Pocket divided into three by two lines of stitching

Try the apron patterns against you before cutting them out and make them longer or wider if you want.

Tie sewn on to back of apron

This pocket is divided in two by a line of stitching.

Cook's apron

Wear this apron to protect your clothes when you are cooking. Keep useful kitchen tools at hand in the apron pocket.

OUTDOOR SURVIVAL KIT

Exploring the great outdoors is exciting, but it is important that you are properly kitted before you go. Wear comfortable clothes and shoes and pack everything else you need, such as food, maps, and a waterproof anorak in a rucksack. Here are all the essential items you will need, together with ideas for things you might find useful for some nature detective work.

Being prepared
Plan your route before you go, and listen to the weather forecast in the morning so that you know what to wear and what to take with you.

Headgear
A woolly hat keeps your head warm in cold weather. When it is hot, a peaked cap shades your eyes and helps to prevent sunstroke.

Peaked cap

Woolly hat

Pocket compass★

Waterproof anorak

Finding the way
Take a map and a compass to help you find your way. Be sure to let your parents know where you are going and how long you expect to be out.

Rucksack
The best rucksacks have lots of useful pockets.

Money belt
A money belt is useful for keeping coins and small items handy.

Maps and plastic wallet

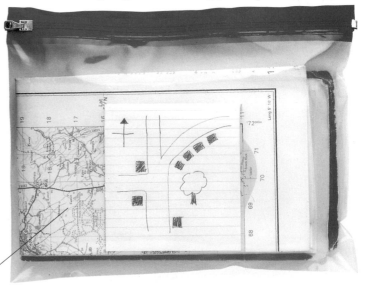

A plastic wallet will keep your maps dry.

What to take

Here are some suggestions for things to carry. Some are essential, such as food and drink, some will help you in case of an accident, and others will help you to study things that you see.

Take some water or juice to drink.

Sweets and chocolate will give you energy.

First-aid kit

Plastic lunch box

Flask

Rations and supplies
If you are going out for longer than half a day, you will need food and drink to keep you going.

Carry coins and useful phone numbers in a small purse in case you need to phone for help.

Protect your skin on sunny days.

Tissues

Sun cream

Torch

Purse

Other essentials
A first-aid kit, tissues, money, a torch, and sun cream are all important extras to take with you.

Nature spotting
When you are out walking, you may want to make notes and sketches of insects, flowers, and birds, or collect any interesting finds. The items shown here will help you.

Take a small camera with you in case you see anything unusual.

Camera

Plastic bags and containers

Notebook and pencil

Pair of binoculars

Carry some containers for collecting specimens.

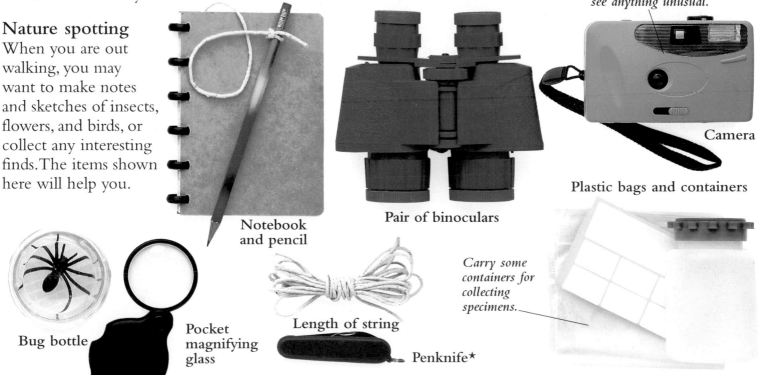

Bug bottle

Pocket magnifying glass

Length of string

Penknife★

RATIONS AND SUPPLIES

Whether you are going on a day's hike, a secret expedition, or just into the park you will get hungry and need rations to keep you going. What food you take will be limited by how you are going to carry it, but every good picnic has the same basic elements: something savoury, something sweet, a drink, and some treats to nibble.

Savoury fillers
Make a roll or sandwich the main part of your rations and fill it with your favourite things. Try not to overfill it so that it is easy to eat, and wrap it in foil or clingfilm to keep it fresh.

Tuna, mayonnaise, and cucumber roll

Roll filled with salami, sliced cheese, and salad

Pitta bread stuffed with salami, sliced cucumber, and tomato

Small French stick filled with sliced ham and salad

Bunches of grapes

Apple

Sweet things
Biscuits and small pieces of cake are good for picnics and do not take up much room in your bag. Take more than you think you need and add some pieces of fresh fruit.

Chocolate brownies

Pear

Shortbread biscuits

Clementine

Savoury extras

If you are going on a special picnic, you could take along salad or vegetable sticks in small containers, and small individually wrapped cheeses.

Sticks of pepper, cucumber, and carrot

Thirst quenchers

Take as much drink as you can carry. Water and fruit juice are more refreshing than fizzy drinks. In cold weather you could take a hot drink or soup in a flask. Make sure you screw on the lids of drinks tightly.

Water bottle filled with fruit juice

Small vacuum flask for cold or hot drinks, or soup

Different small cheeses

Quick snacks and nibbles

It is a good idea to pack a few snacks and quick treats. Put them in one of the pockets of your rucksack. Remember to take the wrappers home with you.

Crisps

Nuts and raisins

Sweets

Mini chocolate bars

Packing your rations

If you are going on a hike, you will need to pack your food in a small lunch box and put it in your rucksack. For a picnic you could use a picnic basket or cool bag. Or why not make your own traveller's bundle for a picnic in the park or garden?

Traveller's bundle on a stick

Small picnic basket

MAKING A MAP

Being able to find your way about is a vital outdoor skill, and you will find it useful to know how to follow or draw a simple map. A map is a bird's eye view of an area. It shows you the way to go from one place to another, what the land looks like and where things are. Here and over the page you can find out how to draw a route map, a picture map, and a treasure map.

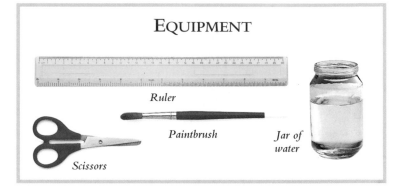

EQUIPMENT

Ruler

Scissors

Paintbrush

Jar of water

You will need

Pocket compass★

Thick paper

Poster paints (or coloured pencils or crayons)

Felt pen

Notebook and pencil

Simple route map

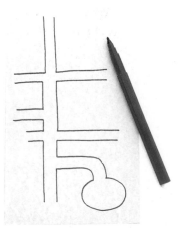

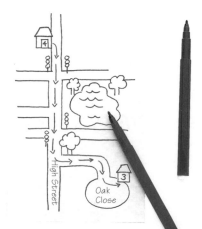

1 Start by drawing the main roads between your home and a friend's house. Show where the smaller side roads join on to them.

2 Draw in the two houses or flats at each end of the route and add any helpful landmarks, such as traffic lights, big trees, or a pond.

3 Write on the house numbers and put in the names of the most important roads. Then draw a line of arrows to show the best route to follow.

Picture map

1 Find a spot outdoors with a good view of your chosen area and sketch a map in your notebook, showing all the main landmarks.

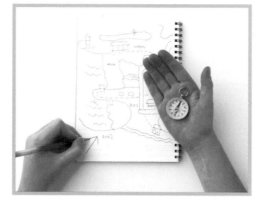

2 Stay in the same place, and find out which way is North with your pocket compass. Draw an arrow on your map pointing in that direction.

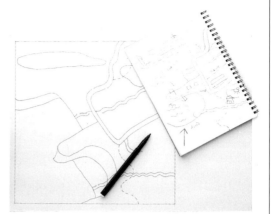

3 Back home, turn the sketch so that the North arrow points straight up and copy the map in this position on to a sheet of paper.

Creating a map key

Most maps use picture symbols to give you information about the area and in one corner there is usually a "key" to tell you what the pictures mean. Make a list of the things you want to show on your map and draw a symbol to represent each one.

Here are some symbols for the sort of things you might want to put on a map of a seaside village.

Steep hill · Pebble beach · Road · Postbox

Farmland · Cliff · Church · Hotel

River · Coniferous wood · Ice-cream stall · Lighthouse

Sea · Deciduous wood · Café · Bus stop

Sandy beach · Footpath · Telephone box · Viewpoint

Filling in the details

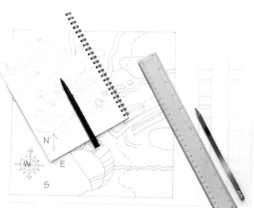

4 In one corner of the map, mark in the points of the compass. Draw boxes for the key picture symbols at one side of the map.

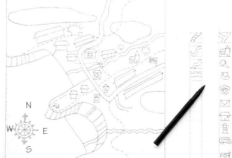

5 Still using your sketch map as reference, draw the picture symbols in place on the map itself and in the boxes for the key.

6 Colour in your map making sure the symbols on it match those in the key. Then add place names to the map and label the key symbols.

FINDING THE WAY

The finished route map shows the quickest route between two places. The picture map will also help you to find your way around, but it gives other information as well, as does the treasure island map. To follow a map, turn it so that the symbols on it, especially the paths or roads, line up with what you see in front of you. Then you are ready to set off!

Route map

If someone asks you the way, it is often better to draw a quick map than to try to give directions. Practise drawing route maps to interesting places in your area.

Traffic lights are good landmarks in towns. Make sure you put them in the right place on the map.

Label the names of the main roads to follow on your map.

Drawing the route in a different colour helps to make it clearer.

Picture map

A map like this of a favourite place or a holiday destination is a great record of where you have been as well as a wonderful picture.

Make the compass decorative if you wish. This one is based on a ship's wheel.

Treasure map

Why not make up your own map of a treasure island? To make it look like an old map, paint the paper with cold black tea or coffee.

To make your map look even older, try drawing it using a black or brown pen with a thin nib.

Crease the paper several times after drawing the map, to make it look worn.

Make up spooky place names and write them on in old-fashioned looking writing.

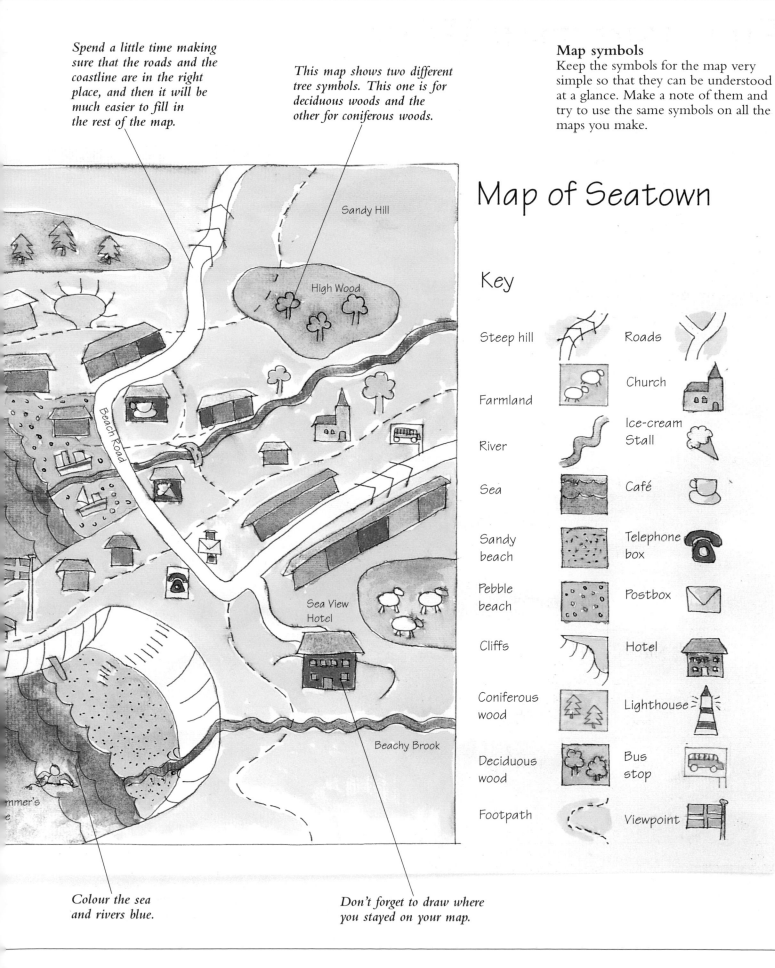

Spend a little time making sure that the roads and the coastline are in the right place, and then it will be much easier to fill in the rest of the map.

This map shows two different tree symbols. This one is for deciduous woods and the other for coniferous woods.

Map symbols
Keep the symbols for the map very simple so that they can be understood at a glance. Make a note of them and try to use the same symbols on all the maps you make.

Map of Seatown

Sandy Hill

High Wood

Beach Road

Sea View Hotel

Beachy Brook

mmer's
e

Key

Steep hill		Roads	
Farmland		Church	
River		Ice-cream Stall	
Sea		Café	
Sandy beach		Telephone box	
Pebble beach		Postbox	
Cliffs		Hotel	
Coniferous wood		Lighthouse	
Deciduous wood		Bus stop	
Footpath		Viewpoint	

Colour the sea and rivers blue.

Don't forget to draw where you stayed on your map.

35

ON THE TRAIL

Tracking skills can be really useful for finding your way about. Here you can find out how to lay and follow a trail using different materials. Choose things that will show up on the ground and collect enough of them for the whole trail. Then you can have fun with your friends laying a simple trail or inventing one with coded signs to follow.

A trail code

You will need a friend to lay a trail for you to follow. If you use a coded trail, you must both agree what the signs mean and keep a record of them in your notebook. Here are some useful signs made with sticks, stones, and leaves.

You will need

(Any one of the following things)

Evergreen or brightly coloured leaves

Strips of old fabric

Stones and pebbles

A notebook to record your trail code

Small straight twigs

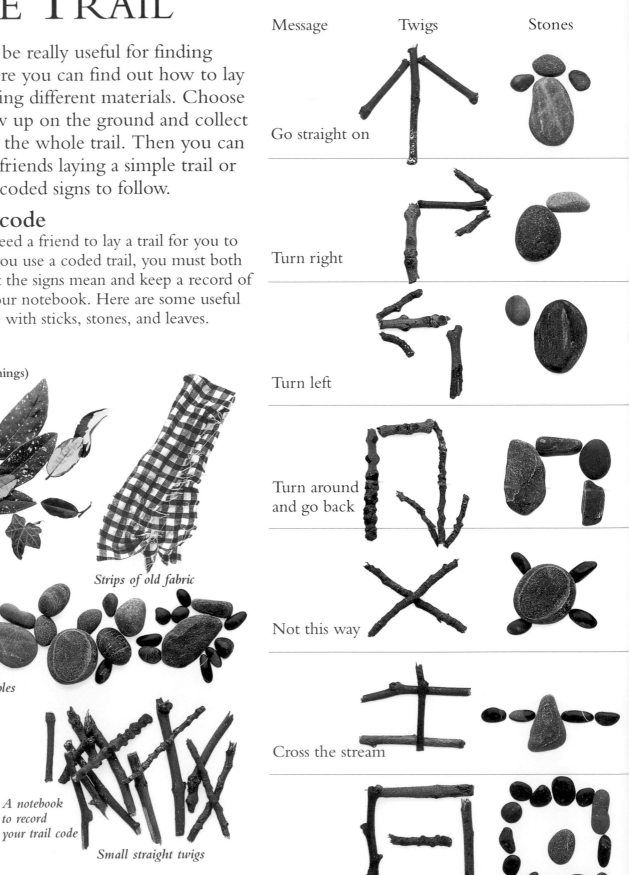

Message	Twigs	Stones
Go straight on		
Turn right		
Turn left		
Turn around and go back		
Not this way		
Cross the stream		
Go home		

Leaves

Plain trails
You do not have to lay a coded trail. You could make simple direction arrows on the ground with leaves, twigs, or stones.

Tell-tale signs
You could tie strips of fabric to bushes or low-lying branches to show which way to go. Remember to remove them all and take them home afterwards.

Direction arrow made from pebbles

Trail Game

Why not play a trail game? You will need at least two people to lay and follow a trail, but it is more fun if there are four of you so that you can work together in pairs. Two of you lay the trail and the other two have to see if they can follow it all the way to the end.

Before you start, work out the trail code together so that you all know what the signs mean. Give the trail layers a ten minute headstart or, if the trail is going to be around a garden, let them finish laying it before the followers set off. And no peeping!

Laying the trail
Always lay the signs on the same side of the path and put them where they show up. Space them about five metres apart so that the followers do not have too far to go between each one.

Make sure you lay the signs very clearly at any tricky spots, such as where a path forks or where the grass grows long.

Direction arrow made from leaves

37

GOING FISHING

Here you can find out how to make a simple fishing rod and drop net for your fishing expeditions. Use the rod to catch fish from a riverbank or from a pier. A drop net is good for catching crabs and other small shellfish from rock pools.

You will need

For the rod

Cork

Garden cane 2 m long

Coloured tape

For the drop net

Cubes of bread and cheese for bait

Embroidery hoops 35 cm across

3 m thick thread or nylon fishing line

Enamel paint

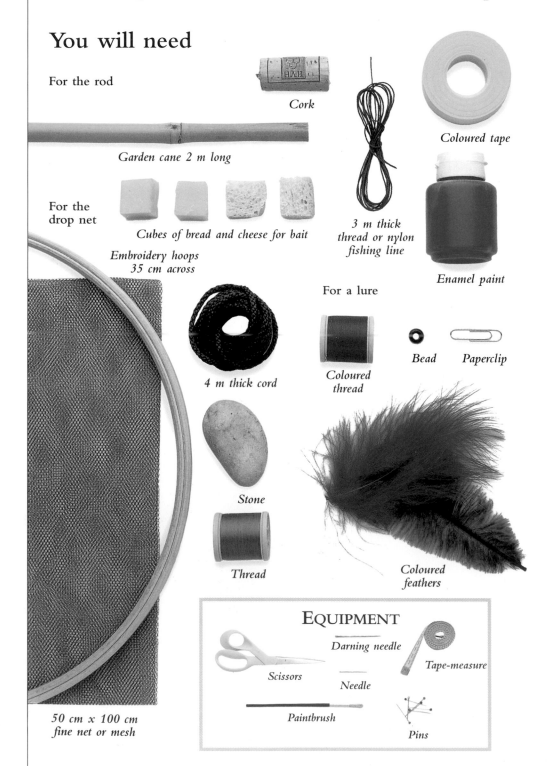

4 m thick cord

For a lure

Coloured thread

Bead   *Paperclip*

Stone

Thread

Coloured feathers

50 cm x 100 cm fine net or mesh

EQUIPMENT

Darning needle

Scissors

Tape-measure

Needle

Paintbrush

Pins

Making the drop net

1 Fold the net in half (50 cm x 50 cm). Pin along two sides, leaving one side open. Sew★ along the pinned sides, about 1 cm in from the edge.

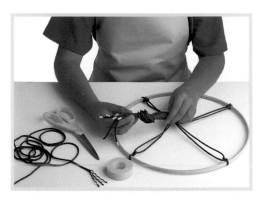

2 To make a handle, cut four pieces of cord each 1 m long. Tie them to the outside embroidery hoop, and then tie the loose ends together.

3 Tie a stone at the bottom of the net. Fold the top of the net over the inside hoop and ask an adult to help fit the other hoop over it.

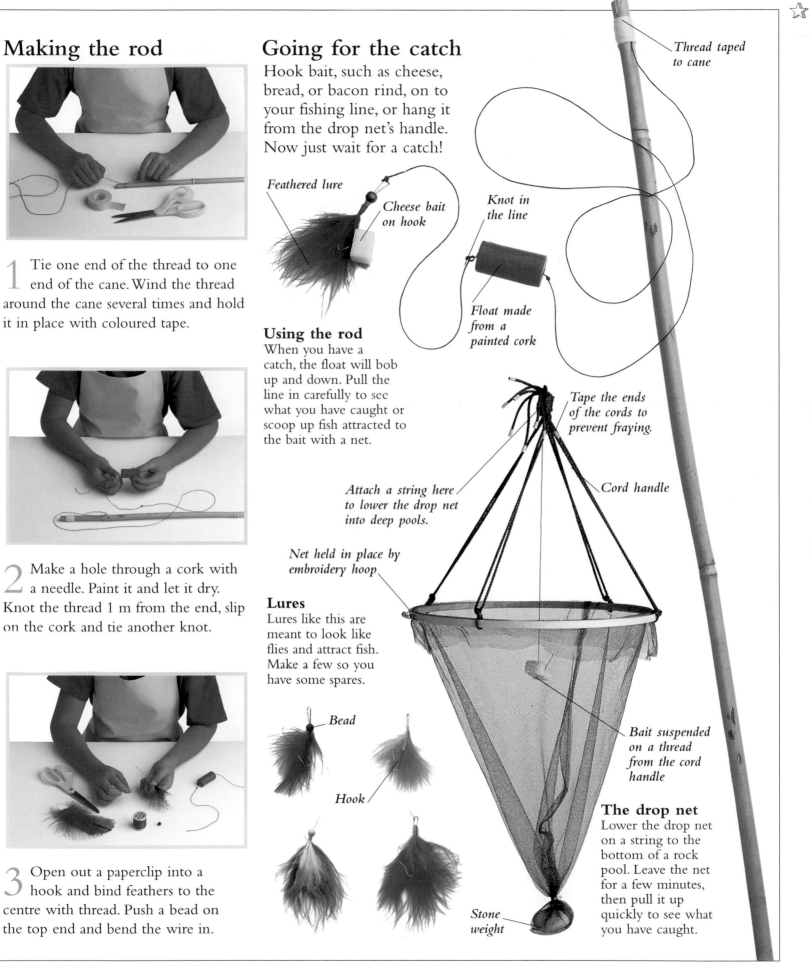

Making the rod

1 Tie one end of the thread to one end of the cane. Wind the thread around the cane several times and hold it in place with coloured tape.

2 Make a hole through a cork with a needle. Paint it and let it dry. Knot the thread 1 m from the end, slip on the cork and tie another knot.

3 Open out a paperclip into a hook and bind feathers to the centre with thread. Push a bead on the top end and bend the wire in.

Going for the catch

Hook bait, such as cheese, bread, or bacon rind, on to your fishing line, or hang it from the drop net's handle. Now just wait for a catch!

Feathered lure

Cheese bait on hook

Using the rod

When you have a catch, the float will bob up and down. Pull the line in carefully to see what you have caught or scoop up fish attracted to the bait with a net.

Lures

Lures like this are meant to look like flies and attract fish. Make a few so you have some spares.

Bead

Hook

Knot in the line

Float made from a painted cork

Thread taped to cane

Tape the ends of the cords to prevent fraying.

Attach a string here to lower the drop net into deep pools.

Cord handle

Net held in place by embroidery hoop

Bait suspended on a thread from the cord handle

The drop net

Lower the drop net on a string to the bottom of a rock pool. Leave the net for a few minutes, then pull it up quickly to see what you have caught.

Stone weight

UNDER COVER

Being able to build a simple shelter is a useful survival skill, and it can also be great fun to do in your own garden. You can make a wigwam from canes and a large piece of material. It is easier to make if you have a friend with you. Or why not make a portable hide to watch animals and birds closely without them seeing you? Turn the page to see the finished wigwam and hide.

EQUIPMENT

Ruler

Scissors

Felt pen

5 cm paintbrush

Jars of water

You will need

For the hide

3 garden canes, 1.22 m long

A piece of calico or old sheet, 5 m x 1.5 m

A piece of calico or sheeting, 1.35 m x 96 cm

String

For the wigwam

5 canes, 60 cm long

String

1 cane, 45 cm long

Large, strong elastic bands

Large pots of poster paint or fabric paint

6 garden canes, 2 m long

Making the wigwam

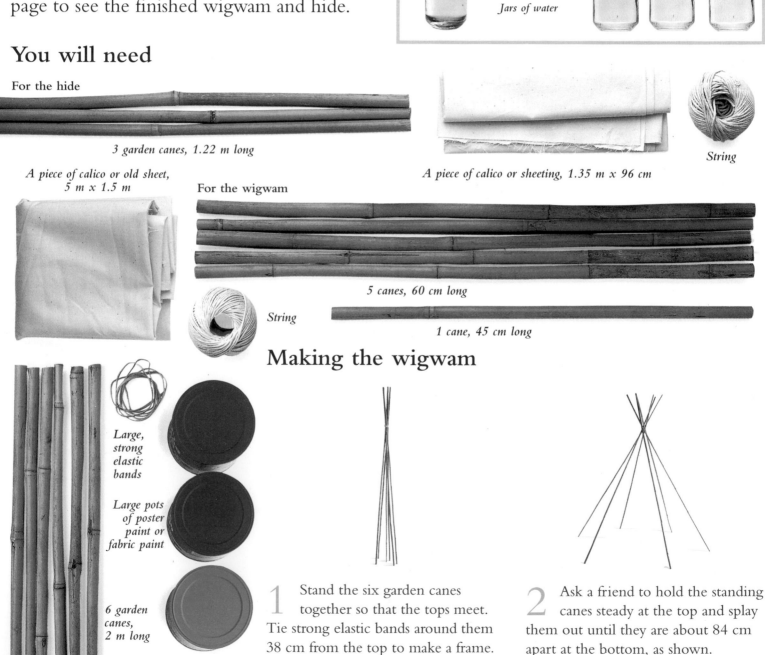

1 Stand the six garden canes together so that the tops meet. Tie strong elastic bands around them 38 cm from the top to make a frame.

2 Ask a friend to hold the standing canes steady at the top and splay them out until they are about 84 cm apart at the bottom, as shown.

3 Use a length of string to tie each of the five 60 cm canes to a long cane so they cross. Wind the string around the canes and tie a reef knot.★

4 Position the five 60 cm canes about 63 cm up from the bottom of each of the long, standing canes, as shown. Leave a space for an opening.

5 Tie the 45 cm cane across the last two long canes, about 85 cm down from the elastic bands, to make the door frame of the wigwam.

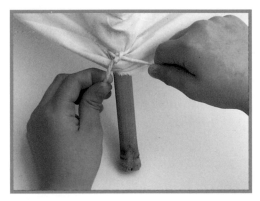

6 Ask a friend to hold the fabric half over the door of the wigwam. Wrap the fabric around the canes so that the two ends meet at the door.

7 Bunch the fabric in where the canes are tied together at the top. Wind a piece of string tightly around the fabric and tie a reef knot.

8 Pull the fabric down each cane. Tie it at the bottom by cutting two holes in the fabric and tying the string through them around the canes.

9 Tie the fabric to the canes in the same way at the points where the shorter canes are tied to the long canes and at the top of each side of the door.

10 Mix paint and water in jars and use a large paintbrush to paint the wigwam fabric with bold shapes, such as circles and crosses.

11 Paint a decorative border along the bottom and around the door opening to complete the wigwam design.

★ *Turn to page 232 to find out how to tie a reef knot.*

SIMPLE SHELTERS

Making the hide

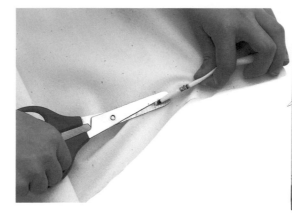

1 Spread out fabric for the hide flat on the ground. Lay the three canes across it as shown, with one at each end and one in the middle.

2 With a pen, make marks on both sides of each cane near the top, the bottom, and in the centre. Then cut a small hole at each mark.

3 Thread a piece of string through each set of holes and round the cane between them. Then knot the strings to fix the fabric to the canes.

Invisible observers

From behind your hide you can watch wildlife close-up. Take a rug to sit on and have your binoculars and notebook handy. Remember to keep as quiet as you possibly can.

Heading home

To take the hide home, pull it out of the ground, fold it in half along the centre cane and roll it up.

Make sure the slits are big enough for your binoculars.

Setting up

To set up the hide, stretch it out to its full width and push each cane into the ground. If the ground is hard, ask an adult to help you. The hide is big enough to conceal two people. You can paint your hide green and brown to camouflage it.

Closed wigwam

When the door of the wigwam is closed, the two ends of the fabric should meet halfway across the opening. The wigwam is not waterproof, so remember to put it away at night or when it rains.

4 Draw two letter-box slits on the fabric halfway between the centre and each outer cane and 25 cm down from the top edge. Cut out the slits.

You can copy these decorations for your wigwam or try out ideas of your own.

Setting up camp

Choose a flat, dry place to set up your wigwam and then splay out the canes until the fabric is fairly taut. Put a waterproof rug inside to make it cosy, and stock it with the supplies you need.

Fold the fabric flaps back around the door canes when you want the door open.

BIRD TABLE

The best way to find out about birds is to put out food for them so that you can watch them close-up. Here and over the page you can find out how to make a bird table, gourmet bird food, and some great bird feeders. You will need an adult's help to make the bird table.

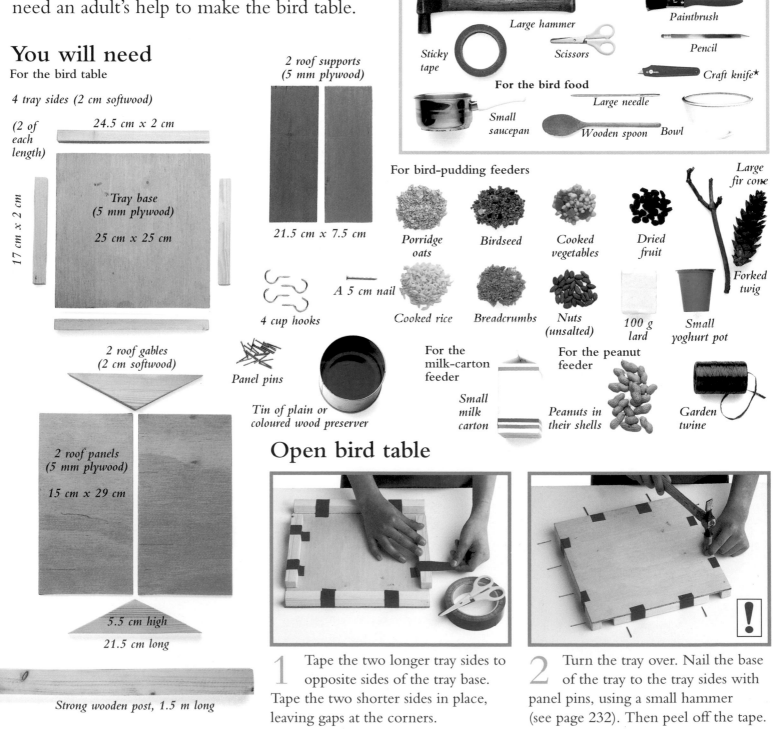

EQUIPMENT

For the bird tables

Small hammer

Ruler

Large hammer

Paintbrush

Sticky tape

Scissors

Pencil

Craft knife ★

For the bird food

Small saucepan

Large needle

Wooden spoon

Bowl

You will need

For the bird table

4 tray sides (2 cm softwood)

(2 of each length)

24.5 cm x 2 cm

17 cm x 2 cm

Tray base (5 mm plywood)

25 cm x 25 cm

2 roof supports (5 mm plywood)

21.5 cm x 7.5 cm

2 roof gables (2 cm softwood)

2 roof panels (5 mm plywood)

15 cm x 29 cm

5.5 cm high

21.5 cm long

Strong wooden post, 1.5 m long

4 cup hooks

A 5 cm nail

Panel pins

Tin of plain or coloured wood preserver

For bird-pudding feeders

Porridge oats

Birdseed

Cooked vegetables

Dried fruit

Large fir cone

Cooked rice

Breadcrumbs

Nuts (unsalted)

100 g lard

Small yoghurt pot

Forked twig

For the milk-carton feeder

Small milk carton

For the peanut feeder

Peanuts in their shells

Garden twine

Open bird table

1 Tape the two longer tray sides to opposite sides of the tray base. Tape the two shorter sides in place, leaving gaps at the corners.

2 Turn the tray over. Nail the base of the tray to the tray sides with panel pins, using a small hammer (see page 232). Then peel off the tape.

3 Draw diagonal lines across the tray to find the centre. Ask an adult to nail the tray to the post with a 5 cm nail where the lines cross.

4 Screw two cup hooks into each of the longer sides of the tray. Then ask an adult to set up the bird table in the garden.

1 Follow steps 1 and 2 for the open bird table. Then measure and draw a pencil line 2 cm in from each side of the two roof pieces.

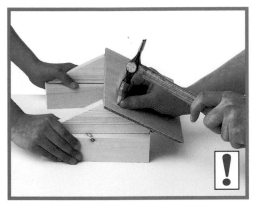

2 Rest the roof gables on blocks of wood. Nail the roof panels on to the gables, lining up the gables inside the pencil lines you have drawn.

3 Hold the roof against a table. Nail one of the roof supports to the centre of a gable with panel pins. Do the same at the other side.

4 Stand the tray and roof on their sides. Nail the roof supports to the outer edges of the short tray sides. Then nail the tray to the post*.

Yoghurt-pot feeder

1 Melt the lard in a saucepan over a low heat. Put the rest of the food in a bowl and pour the melted lard over it. Mix it in well.

2 Spoon the pudding mixture into the yoghurt pot. Push the twig into the mixture, then leave the pudding until it sets hard.

3 When the pudding has set, pull it out of the yoghurt pot by the twig and roll it in birdseed. Tie a piece of string to the twig.

Ask an adult to do this, as for Step 3 for the open bird table. **45**

BIRD WATCH

Peanut feeder

Thread a big needle with a double length of garden twine. Knot the ends of the twine together, then thread the peanuts on to it.

Milk-carton feeder

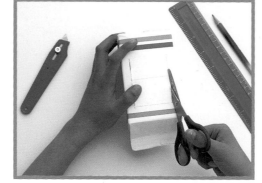

1 Draw a rectangle, with a line across it a third of the way up, on the front of the milk carton. Cut along the sides and top of the rectangle.

2 Cut along the middle line and bend back the flap along the bottom line of the rectangle. Do the same on the back of the carton.

Bird patrol

The more you watch birds, the easier it will become to recognise common ones. Find out which birds visit your local area first, then try bird-watching in woods, by a river, or by the sea. It helps to make quick sketches. Look out for a bird's colour, size, the shape of its beak, wings, and feet, and any special features.

Draw ovals for the body and head.

Add the beak and tail.

Then fill in the wings and feet.

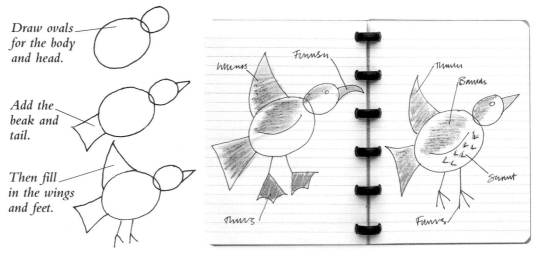

Lying low

If you are bird-watching, it is very important to lie still and keep quiet so that you do not frighten away the birds. You could make a hide and watch from there (see page 40).

What was it?

If you don't recognise a bird, draw a sketch of it and make some notes to help you look it up in a field guide back at home.

A closer look

It is a good idea to carry binoculars with you so that you can look closely at any birds you see.

Feeding the birds

Ask an adult to paint the bird table with wood preservative and to set it up in the garden. Make sure there are no hiding places nearby where cats might lie in wait to pester the birds! Then hang up the feeders you have made and put out some tasty titbits!

This bird table has been stained with green wood preservative to stop it from rotting.

Stale cakes, bread, and biscuits, old cheese, bacon rinds, and unsalted nuts are all good scraps for birds.

The gaps at the corners of the table allow rainwater to drain away.

Open bird table
You can add any of the feeders to the open bird table in the same way as for the covered one. Check the food on this table after it has rained and replace anything that has gone soggy.

Fir-cone feeder
Push bird pudding into the cracks of a large fir cone to make this feeder.

Yoghurt-pot feeder
Hang this feeder from the bird table and watch the birds sway as they feed from it.

Peanut feeder
Tie up the peanut feeder and watch the birds crack open the nuts with their beaks.

Milk carton-feeder
Make a hole in the top of the milk carton feeder and tie string through it. Fill the feeder with birdseed.

This flap makes a perch for the birds to stand on as they feed.

WILDLIFE HABITATS

To attract wildlife into your garden, set up some mini-habitats. Here and over the page you can find out how to make a bee and butterfly garden, build a log pile habitat, set up insect traps, and keep minibeast records in a nature notebook and chart. Start the bee and butterfly garden in spring so that you can watch it grow and attract insects over the summer months.

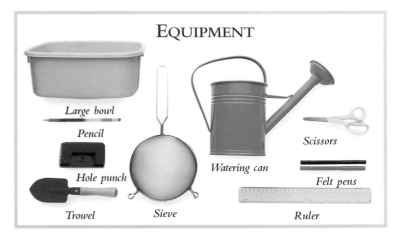

EQUIPMENT

Large bowl

Pencil

Hole punch

Trowel

Sieve

Watering can

Scissors

Felt pens

Ruler

You will need

For the log-pile habitat

Large brick

Soil

Bark and twigs

Fern

Primula

Logs

Ivy

For the insect traps

Small tile

Miniature flowerpot

Grapefruit

Potato

Bacon rind and bread

For the bee and butterfly garden

Four small stones

Yoghurt pot

Dry leaves

Lavender

For the chart and notebook

Sticky tape

Strong glue

Thyme

Cord

Spiral-bound notebook

Coloured pencils

Bug bottle

Green, white, and yellow card

Thin ribbon

Small leaves

Sunflower seeds

Flowerpot and saucer

Log-pile habitat

1 You can make this in a corner of the garden, or in a window box. Stack and arrange some logs, bricks, and bark on the soil.

2 Plant the ivy, fern, primula, and any other plants to create a natural environment. Fill in empty areas with dead leaves and small twigs.

3 To make a pitfall trap, scoop out a hole in the ground and sink the yoghurt pot into it. Drop some bacon rinds into the pot as bait.

4 Lay the four stones around the top of the yoghurt pot, as shown. Place a small tile on top of the stones so that it is raised above the pot rim.

5 To make hideaways for insects and other creepy crawlies, stuff flowerpots with dead leaves. Lay the pots on their sides.

6 For extra traps, cut a grapefruit in half, scoop out the middle and put cubes of bread in it. Do the same with a potato. Place it in the habitat.

Bee and butterfly garden

1 To repot a plant, put some soil in the bottom of a new, larger pot. Gently remove the plant and soil from its old pot, as shown.

2 Lower the plant into the new flowerpot, then fill the pot with soil. Press the soil down firmly around the plant and water it well.

3 For the sunflowers, fill a pot with soil. Push five sunflower seeds into the soil about 1 cm deep. Water the soil and keep it well watered.

NATURE SURVEY

Nature chart

Decorate some card and make a chart by drawing grids on some paper. With the hole punch make a hole and attach the grids to the card with cord.

Studying minibeasts

1 Try sifting some soil and leaves from the log-pile area into a large bowl. How many types of minibeast can you find left in the sieve?

2 Put any creatures you find in the bug bottle to study them. Draw them accurately and then put them back where you found them.

Wildlife in the garden

Keep a regular watch on the log-pile habitat and bee and butterfly garden to see how many creatures are attracted to them. Practise making quick sketches of creatures you find. To find out more about the minibeasts, you could look them up in a reference book.

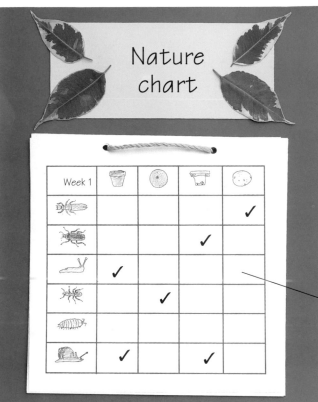

Nature chart

Grids

Insect-trap chart

Draw the traps at the top of the chart and the creatures you find on the left-hand side. Use the chart to record those creatures you have found in the insect traps by ticking the correct box. You could add the time and date that you found the insects.

Log-pile habitat

Carefully lift logs and bricks and look under dead leaves to find out which creatures have moved into your log pile. Keep a regular check on the insect traps and make a note of what you find there. Make sure you release any minibeasts caught in the traps.

Nature notebook

Make sketches of insects in your notebook. Start with three circles for the head, thorax, and abdomen. Then add legs, wings or wing cases, antennae, and any special features.

Ivy

Large brick

Head

Abdomen

Garden
minibeasts

Thorax

Bee and butterfly garden
Plant this garden in spring. Place the
pots in a sunny spot and water them to
keep the soil damp. Butterflies and bees
are attracted to most plants with flowers,
so you could use other flowering plants
for the garden instead.

Bee

Butterfly

Primula

Thyme

Sunflowers

Lavender

Fern

Twigs

Potato trap

Log

Grapefruit trap

Pitfall trap

Flowerpot
hideaway

NATURE LOGBOOK

Your nature logbook is your own record of all the things you see, find, and collect on your expeditions outdoors. You can draw in it, stick in unusual treasures, put in pressed plants, magazine cuttings, or photographs you have taken, and keep records of surveys or experiments you have done. To make your logbook really special, why not make the book yourself with different sorts of card and paper? Below you can see what to do.

The cover
Stick a picture on to the cover and add a torn paper square for the title.

Roughly knot the raffia, to give the book a natural look.

Sam's Nature Logbook

EQUIPMENT

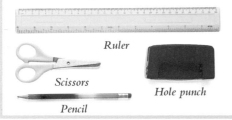

Ruler

Scissors

Hole punch

Pencil

Choose a stick slightly longer than the height of the book.

Draw a picture to stick on to the front cover of your book.

You will need

Raffia

2 sheets of thick, coloured card

A variety of sheets of paper and tracing paper

A straight stick
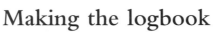

Making the logbook

1 Cut two rectangles of card for the cover. For the pages, cut the paper into slightly smaller rectangles. Punch holes through all the sheets, as shown.

2 Put the paper inside the covers, lining up the holes. Tie pieces of raffia through the holes and around the stick to hold the book together.

Expedition notebook
The notes you make in your expedition notebook will provide lots of material for your logbook. Copy things out giving details of the dates and places.

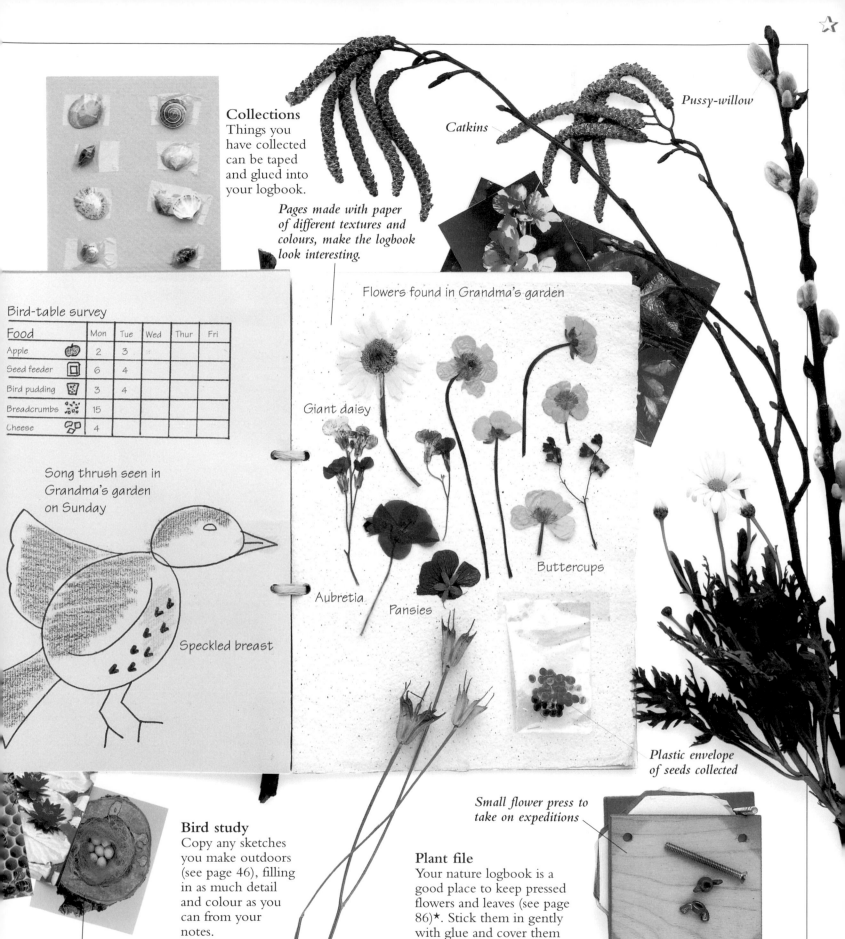

Collections
Things you have collected can be taped and glued into your logbook.

Pages made with paper of different textures and colours, make the logbook look interesting.

Catkins

Pussy-willow

Flowers found in Grandma's garden

Giant daisy

Buttercups

Aubretia

Pansies

Bird-table survey

Food		Mon	Tue	Wed	Thur	Fri
Apple		2	3			
Seed feeder		6	4			
Bird pudding		3	4			
Breadcrumbs		15				
Cheese		4				

Song thrush seen in Grandma's garden on Sunday

Speckled breast

Plastic envelope of seeds collected

Bird study
Copy any sketches you make outdoors (see page 46), filling in as much detail and colour as you can from your notes.

Collect pictures of birds and insects.

Small flower press to take on expeditions

Plant file
Your nature logbook is a good place to keep pressed flowers and leaves (see page 86)★. Stick them in gently with glue and cover them with a sheet of tracing paper to protect them.

★*Remember – never pick or uproot wild plants.* **53**

WEATHER STATION

Is it going to be hot or cold today? Will it rain or stay dry? The weather changes all the time but you can learn to spot the signs of what it might do next. Here you can find out how to set up your own weather station and keep a record of the weather each day. Below you can see how to make a raincatcher and a wind vane. Over the page you can find out how to use them and keep a weather chart.

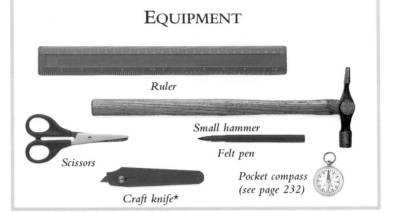

EQUIPMENT

Ruler

Scissors

Small hammer

Felt pen

Craft knife★

Pocket compass (see page 232)

You will need

For the wind vane

Strong glue

Pin

A piece of dowelling about 25 cm long

A plastic tub with a lid　　*A plastic drinking straw*

Some stones or pebbles　　*Sand*　　*Pieces of thin coloured plastic, cut from containers*

Sticky tape in two different colours

For the raincatcher

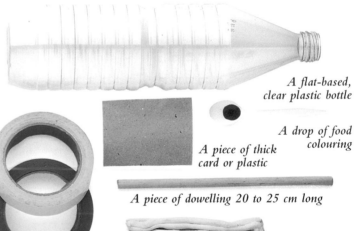

A flat-based, clear plastic bottle

A drop of food colouring

A piece of thick card or plastic

A piece of dowelling 20 to 25 cm long

Modelling clay

Making the raincatcher

1　Cut off the bottom half of the bottle. Then cut off the funnel part of the top of the bottle. You will not need the middle section.

2　Slide the top part of the bottle upside down into the base of the bottle, to act like a funnel. Stick the bottle edges together with tape.

3　Roll the modelling clay into a long sausage and press it around the base of the raincatcher. Use this to hold the raincatcher in place outside.

4 Put a drop of food colouring into the bottle so that the rainwater you catch will be coloured and you will be able to see it clearly.

5 To make a dipstick, hold the piece of dowelling against a ruler. Use a felt pen to make centimetre marks along half of the stick.

6 For decoration, wind sticky tape around the top part of the stick. Cut a cloud shape out of card, colour it and tape it to the top of the stick.

Making the wind vane

1 Make a hole in the lid of the plastic tub with a craft knife. Wind sticky tape, in two colours, around the dowelling to decorate it.

2 Hold the stick upright in the centre of the tub and fill the tub with stones and sand. Slide the lid over the stick and press it on to the tub.

3 Cut four small triangles out of coloured plastic. Then cut out two bigger triangles and two large "V" shapes, as shown in the picture.

4 Glue the four small triangles to the lid of the tub in opposite pairs so that they are pointing in four different directions.

5 Glue the two large triangles together to cover one end of the straw. Glue the "V" shapes together to cover the other end of the straw.

6 Using a hammer, pin the straw to the top of the stick with the map pin so that the straw lies level and can spin freely in the wind.

WEATHER REPORT

Once you have made the raincatcher and the wind vane, you will need to buy a simple thermometer to complete your weather station. Then draw up a weather chart and try to keep a daily record of the weather by studying the sky and using your instruments.

Tape on a piece of ribbon to hang up your chart.

Weather chart

Make a weather chart by drawing a grid, like the one shown below, on some sheets of paper. Use paper fasteners to pin the grids on to a rectangle of stiff card. Draw the weather symbols you are going to use on a strip of paper and glue it along the bottom of the card.

Unfasten the top sheet of paper at the end of each week to give you a new chart for the next week.

Glue on a strip of paper and make a decorative heading.

Paper fasteners hold the grids in place on the card

Weather Chart

Week beginning 25 May	Sunday	Monday	Tuesday	Wednesday	Thursday	Friday	Saturday
Temperature	21°C	18°C	17°C	17°C	19°C		
Wind direction	SW	SW	W	W	NW		
Rainfall	0	0	0	1 cm	0.5 cm		
Weather conditions							

Weather symbols	Clear sky	Some cloud	Cloudy	Windy	Thunder	Rain	Snow	Hail

Use these picture symbols or invent your own to show what the weather is like.

You could add more symbols to show fog, mist, or frost.

Weather station

Set up your weather station outside and use the instruments to find out how much rain falls, what the temperature is, and which way the wind is blowing. Record your findings on your weather chart.

This thermometer shows the temperature in two scales: degrees Celsius (°C) and degrees Fahrenheit (°F).

The top of the blue column of liquid moves up and down to show the air temperature.

0°C marks freezing point.

Raincatcher

Stand the raincatcher in an open space (without its dipstick). Fix it in place with the modelling clay and check it every day to see whether there is any rainwater in it. If there is, dip the stick into it and measure the amount of water.

Put the dipstick upright in the raincatcher.

Measuring rain
The water makes a wet line on the dipstick against the centimetre marks so you can measure how much rain has fallen.

Tip out the water once you have measured it.

Wind vane

Use a compass to find which way is North★. Turn your wind vane so that one triangle points that way.

Map pin

Make sure the arrow can turn freely.

The arrow's pointer points into the wind.

The triangles should point in the four directions of the compass.

Wind direction
The arrow on the wind vane shows you which way the wind is blowing. It points in the direction from which the wind is coming. A north wind, for example, blows from the North.

Mark the triangles North, South, East, and West.

Thermometer

Hang the thermometer in a shady place outside. Look at it at the same time each day and read the number by the top of the column of liquid.

Write down all the readings you take.

★Turn to page 232 to learn how to use a compass.

ALL IN A POT

You can create a beautiful garden anywhere. Flowers, herbs, and even fruit can be grown indoors in pots and window boxes. Start planting today and watch your own garden blossom to life in front of your eyes. Turn the page for lots of interesting mini-garden ideas.

EQUIPMENT

Watering can

Trowel

Scissors

You will need

The basics

Soil-based potting compost★

Gravel or clay pellets

Terracotta or plastic flowerpots

Drip trays

Plastic window box with drainage holes in the bottom, and drip tray

Terracotta window box with holes in the bottom

For an everlasting garden

Dried moss

Dried rosebuds

Dried lavender

Modelling clay

Plant food

For a fruit garden

Young strawberry plants

Plant labels

For a flower garden

Trailing ivy

Geraniums

Busy Lizzies

Striped or plain petunias

For a herb garden

Young herb plants

★It is better to use potting compost than ordinary garden soil.

Preparing for planting

1 Fill the bottom of the window box and flowerpots with a layer of gravel. This will help water to drain out of the pots better.

2 Then half-fill the window box and pots with potting compost. If the compost is very dry, water it lightly before planting anything.

Repotting a plant

Lower the plant into the flowerpot so that the bottom of its stem is just below the pot rim. Fill in the sides with compost and firm it down.

A flower garden

1 Take the plants out of their pots and decide how to arrange them. Start with the tallest plants. They look good at the back of the box.

2 Then add any low, trailing plants. It is best to put these at the front, so that they can grow down over the window box.

3 Arrange the rest of your flowers in the box. Then fill in the gaps between them with more compost and press it down firmly.

An everlasting garden

1 Break off a piece of modelling clay and press it into the bottom of a small flowerpot. This will keep the stems of the dried flowers in place.

2 Trim the stems of the dried flowers. Then start arranging them in the flowerpot by pressing them gently into the modelling clay.

3 When all the dried flowers are in place, arrange a little dried moss around the top of the pot, to make it look as if they are growing naturally.

GARDENS IN POTS

These pots and boxes of brightly coloured flowering plants will cheer up any room or garden. Look for a sunny, sheltered spot to grow your plants, such as outside on a window ledge or inside on a wide shelf or windowsill. A window box is very heavy so you will need to ask an adult to move it.

Dried rose garden

Lavender and rose garden

Lavender garden

Terracotta flowerpot

Dried rose

Dried lavender

Moss

Everlasting flowers

These pretty dried flower gardens will never die. But they should be kept out of direct sunlight or their colours will soon fade.

Red geranium

Yellow plastic pot

A plant a pot

If you haven't got a window box, why not plant a group of plants in matching pots? Stand them in a row for a striking effect.

Ivy

Marjoram

These ivy plants have green and white leaves.

Painted pots

Try growing house plants in brightly painted pots. You can find out how to decorate flowerpots and drip trays on page 12.

This white flower will soon lose its petals, then its centre will swell and ripen to form a strawberry.

Strawberry plants

Tiny, unripe strawberry

Red petunia

Strawberry garden

Early in the summer these strawberry plants are still in flower. If you look closely, you can see small, green strawberries forming. Before long the strawberries will grow and ripen. They are ready to pick when the berries have turned red.

Trailing ivy plant

Green plastic window box and drip tray

White plastic window box and drip tray

Herb garden

Fresh herbs look pretty sitting on a kitchen windowsill and they make the kitchen smell delicious, too. It is best to trim them often, to stop the plants becoming too big. If you grow herbs outside, their flowers will attract bees and butterflies.

Chives

Golden marjoram

Purple sage

Parsley

Growing mint
Mint spreads quickly, so it is a good idea to grow it in its own pot.

Mint

Summer garden

This colourful window box will flower all through the summer. It will need watering once a day, or more often on hot days. Removing dead flowers will make the plants flower for longer.

Terracotta pot with drip tray

Thyme

Pretty terracotta window box

Caring for your plants

Red geranium

Red and white striped petunias

Purple petunia

1 Your pots and window boxes will need watering every day in warm weather. The compost should always feel slightly moist.

Scarlet Busy Lizzies

2 All plants will flower for longer and look better if you dead-head them regularly. This means snipping or picking off any dead flowers.

MINIATURE GARDEN

Here and on the next page you can find out how to create a real miniature garden of your own, complete with its own paving and garden furniture. Below are a selection of some plants you could use but, if you can't find these, use similar plants. For an outdoor garden, the best plants to use are miniatures with tiny flowers and small leaves.

EQUIPMENT

Secateurs*

Large paintbrush

Felt pen

Ruler

Trowel

Small scissors

Large scissors

You will need

For the garden furniture

For the garden

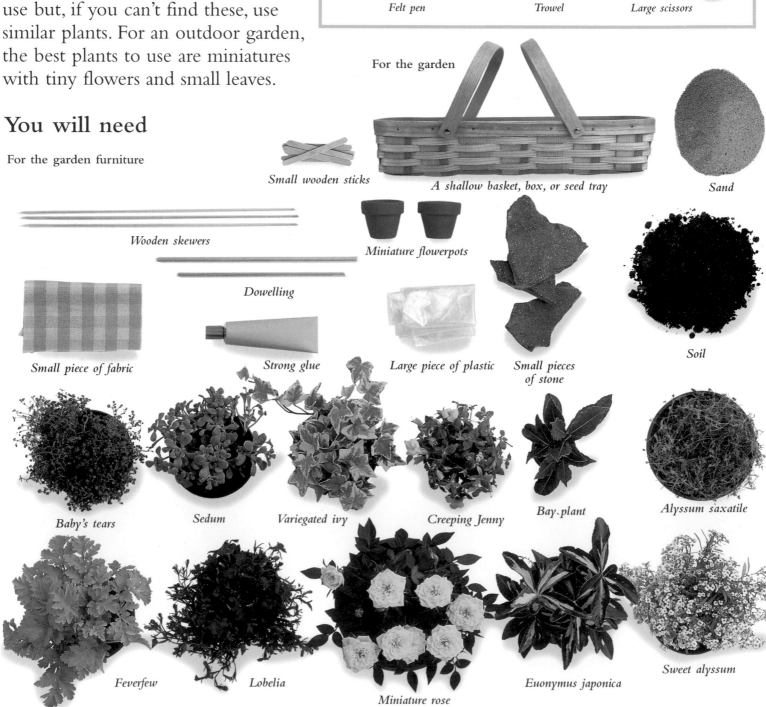

Small wooden sticks

A shallow basket, box, or seed tray

Sand

Wooden skewers

Dowelling

Miniature flowerpots

Soil

Small piece of fabric

Strong glue

Large piece of plastic

Small pieces of stone

Baby's tears

Sedum

Variegated ivy

Creeping Jenny

Bay plant

Alyssum saxatile

Feverfew

Lobelia

Miniature rose

Euonymus japonica

Sweet alyssum

*Ask an adult for help when using secateurs.

Making a deck chair

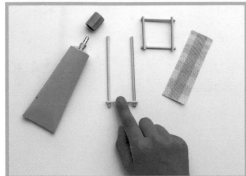

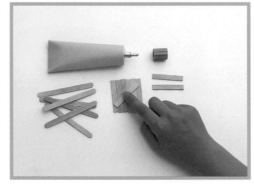

1 Cut★ four 5 cm sticks from a wooden skewer and glue into a square. Glue a 5 cm stick to the end of two sticks 10 cm long, as shown.

2 Glue the square to the sides of the long sticks to make a deck chair frame. Attach a strip of fabric 4 cm x 10 cm in place to make a seat.

Making some trellis

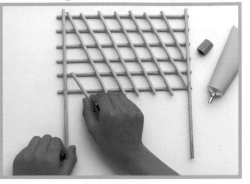

Glue six sticks of dowelling 20 cm long to two sticks 22 cm long. Cut six 13 cm sticks and two 8 cm sticks. Glue diagonally on to the cross sticks.

Making a pyramid

To make a pyramid, join the ends of three pieces of dowelling, 30 cm long. Stick short pieces of dowelling of varying length across them.

Making a table

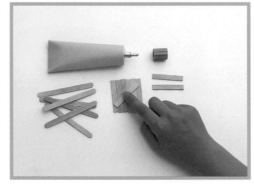

1 Cut★ seven pieces of stick 6 cm long. Put six sticks together for a table top and glue the last stick across them, to hold them together.

2 For legs, glue four 5 cm pieces of dowelling to each end of two 5 cm pieces of wooden stick. Glue the sticks to the table top, as shown.

Making the garden

1 Line the basket with some plastic and cut small holes for drainage. Using the trowel, fill the basket about two-thirds full of soil.

2 Now plan out your garden. Leave the plants in their containers and arrange them in the basket to see where they look best.

3 Decide where to position the trellis, path, and the patio. Make the patio and path by laying large and small stones on the soil.

A SMALL WORLD
Planting the garden

1 Remove the plants from the pots and plant any tall plants. Put the trellis and pyramid in place. Add ivy by the trellis and a rose in the pyramid.

A secret garden

The finished garden is a real world in miniature, with winding paths and shady spots for tables or deck chairs. Stand the garden outside in a bright spot and water it well. It is important to care for your garden and look after your plants all year round. Trim the plants if they get too overgrown, and snip off any dead leaves or flowers. Keep the soil moist by spraying it with water from a spray bottle.

Feverfew

Steps created by laying stones on top of each other

Lobelia

2 To make a lawn, plant creeping, low-growing plants, such as Baby's tears. Carefully press the plants in place.

3 Fill in all the gaps in the garden with small, brightly coloured flowering plants. Lobelia and Sweet alyssum make good fillers.

4 Sprinkle sand over the patio and paths. Use a wide paintbrush to brush the sand into the cracks between the stones.

5 Add the garden furniture. Fill the miniature flowerpots with small flowers or herb plants and position them in the garden.

Snip off any dead flower heads to encourage the plants to keep flowering.

Miniature bay plant in a pot

Miniature rose entwined through pyramid

Ivy woven through trellis

Patio area

Sedum

Sand brushed between stones

Path made of small stones

Cane basket lined with plastic and filled with soil

GIANTS FROM SEEDS

Why not see if you can grow a giant plant from a tiny seed? Sunflowers and pumpkins can both grow to a huge size, if they have the right conditions – and you are patient. Read the seed packets to check they are the giant varieties. Then have a competition with a friend to see who can grow the tallest sunflower or the biggest pumpkin!

EQUIPMENT

Liquid plant food

Felt pen

Watering can

Trowel

You will need

Plant labels

Elastic bands

Sunflower seeds, giant variety

Pumpkin seeds, giant variety

Garden canes

Seed compost

8 cm flower pots with drip trays

Plastic bags

Planting pumpkins

1 Fill the pots with compost and push two or three seeds about 2 cm into it. Water the pots well and label the seeds.

2 Secure plastic bags over the pots with an elastic band and place on a light windowsill. When the first shoots appear, remove the bags.

3 After danger of frost is past, pull out all but the strongest seedling in each pot. Plant the strong seedlings in the garden and water them.

Sowing sunflowers

1 Plant three seeds in each place where you want one plant, as they will not all grow. Push the seeds about 1 cm down into the soil.

2 Label the seeds and water them well. As the seedlings grow, pull out any weak ones so the plants are about 45 cm apart. Support small seedlings with garden canes.

Golden giants

Pumpkins are trailing plants and will need at least two metres each in which to grow. Harvest your pumpkins 12 to 20 weeks after they have been planted.

They are ripe when the skin hardens and the stem cracks. Cut them off their plants and stand them in a bright place for 10 days so the skin hardens further.

Mighty flowers

Sunflowers can grow up to three metres tall. To stop them from falling over, tie each sunflower to a garden cane as it grows taller. Measure the plants every week and keep a record of their heights in your nature logbook (see page 52).

If you want a really tall plant, pinch out any side shoots as they appear. When the seeds are ripe, cut off the sunflower heads, keep the seeds, and save them for planting the following year.

Once the skin has hardened, use your pumpkin for cooking, or scoop out the inside and use the hollow shell as a candle holder.

PLANT A GARDEN

You don't need much space to have a garden. Here and on the next page you can see how to plant a colourful garden of flowers and herbs on a plot that is only one metre square. For an instant garden, use bedding plants (colourful plants which last one summer) mixed with a few longer lasting ones. Or sow seeds in trays in spring and plant them out in the garden in early summer.

EQUIPMENT

Pencil

Scissors

Rake

Spade

Plant spray   Notebook   Watering can   Trowel

Bucket

You will need

An attractive pot for the centrepiece

2 purple sage plants

2 variegated oregano plants

4 golden feverfew, or golden marjoram plants

2 sweet basil plants

1 thyme plant

20 small, purple viola plants

2 pink-flowered strawberry plants

4 white marguerite plants

1 large, pink, perennial geranium plant

2 lilac petunia plants

4 large, yellow viola plants

4 pink dianthus plants

Planting out

1 Decide where you are going to put a plant and dig a hole a little deeper than the plant's container. Check that the hole is big enough.

2 To take a plant out of a pot, tip the plant upside down between your fingers and squeeze the pot at the sides to loosen the compost.

3 Stand the plant in the hole you have dug. Fill in the spaces around it with soil and press the soil down. Then water the plant well.

Planning the garden

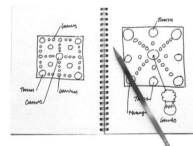

Look at other gardens for ideas. Then draw a plan based on a simple pattern and decide which plants to use.

Preparing the ground

First of all, working from the middle to the edges of the plot, take out the weeds (make sure that you remove all their roots too). Dig over the ground to break up the soil. Then dig in some garden compost to improve the soil. Finally, rake the soil level.

Arranging the plants

When you design your garden, always try to choose plants in colours that go well together.

1 Put the centrepiece in place, then plant the lines of plants that form the framework of your design.

2 Fill in the rest of the garden with plants. Allow enough space around each plant for it to grow.

GARDEN IN BLOOM

Once you have finished creating your garden, it is important to look after the plants all year round. By following the simple steps below you will have a healthy and long-lasting garden. Before buying any plants, check the labels to see what conditions they grow best in.

Watering

Water the plants every day, unless it rains, until they have settled in and started growing. After that only water them if the soil looks dry.

Pest control

Check the garden regularly for signs of pests. Remove snails and spray greenfly or blackfly with a mixture of warm water and washing-up liquid.

Deadheading

Plants will flower for longer if you regularly pick or snip off the dead flower heads. Snip the herbs often to keep them small and bushy.

Gathering herbs

Once your herbs have grown, pick their leaves to cook with. If you use the pink-flowering strawberry plants, the fruit may taste slightly bitter.

Spring bulbs

For a pretty spring garden, plant spring-flowering bulbs between the plants. Plant them in autumn following any instructions.

The finished garden

A white marguerite is planted at each corner.

Golden marjoram

Dianthus

Lilac and yellow viola

Pink-flowering strawberry plant

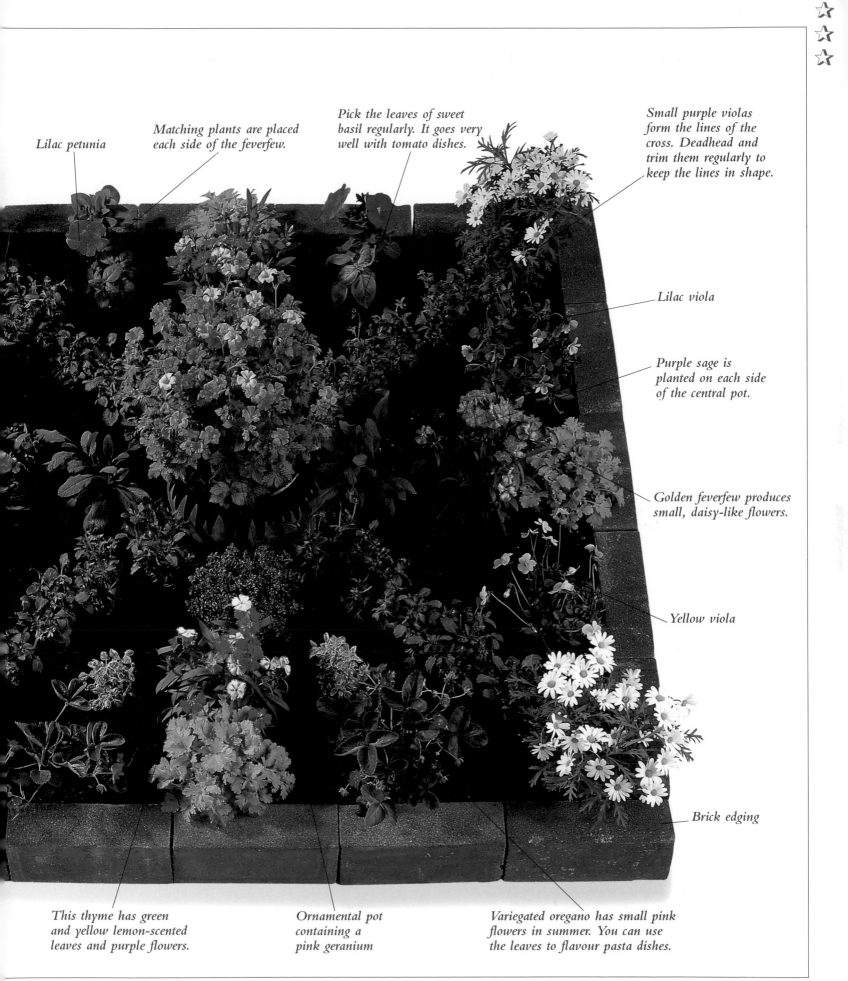

Lilac petunia

Matching plants are placed each side of the feverfew.

Pick the leaves of sweet basil regularly. It goes very well with tomato dishes.

Small purple violas form the lines of the cross. Deadhead and trim them regularly to keep the lines in shape.

Lilac viola

Purple sage is planted on each side of the central pot.

Golden feverfew produces small, daisy-like flowers.

Yellow viola

Brick edging

This thyme has green and yellow lemon-scented leaves and purple flowers.

Ornamental pot containing a pink geranium

Variegated oregano has small pink flowers in summer. You can use the leaves to flavour pasta dishes.

NATURE'S MODELS

On a quiet afternoon, why not try making a model with some of the things you have collected outdoors? With a little imagination you can transform twigs, fir cones, leaves, and feathers into works of art. Here and overleaf you can find out how to create tiny mice, a corn dolly, a wooden seagull, and a sunflower.

EQUIPMENT

Craft knife*

Strong glue

Scissors

Black felt pen

You will need

For the corn dolly

Thick thread

Raffia or long pieces of straw

Evergreen leaves

For the sunflower on a stick

A piece of strong card

Bundle of small, straight twigs

Small fir cones

For the seagull sculpture

2 matching rectangles of flat wood for the body

Flat piece of wood for the base

Shell

A thin, straight stick

Pieces of wood for the head, neck, and beak

Evergreen leaves

Two long, thin twigs

Grey or white feathers

For the fir-cone mice

Pink paper

A medium-sized fir cone for each mouse

Raffia

Small pieces of sea glass or small shells

Corn dolly

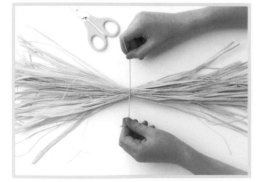

1 Cut about 25 pieces of raffia 25 cm long. Tie them together in the middle with thick thread to make the doll's waist.

2 Divide the raffia below the waist in half in order to make two legs. Tie thread round each leg at the top, in the middle, and near the bottom.

3 Tie thread round the doll's chest, and split the raffia above it into three sections. Tie the two outer sections, as shown, to make arms.

*Ask an adult for help when using a craft knife.

4 Tie thread round the raffia just above the arms to make a neck. Then fold back the raffia and tie it at the neck, as shown, to make the head.

5 Wind pieces of raffia round the doll's body and neck to make them look fatter, then tie the ends and tuck them into the doll's body.

6 Make a dress by tying leaves to the doll's waist with a piece of raffia. Make a hat out of small leaves and attach it to her head.

Seagull sculpture

1 Glue two twigs to one of the matching rectangles of wood for legs. Glue on two tail feathers, then add a small piece of wood for a neck.

2 Glue the other matching wooden rectangle in place over the first, to cover the places where the legs, neck, and tail feathers join the body.

3 Glue a thin piece of wood to the back of the neck for the lower beak. Glue a larger piece of wood to the front of the neck for the head.

4 Glue two feathers to each side of the bird's body for wings, so that the back set of feathers points upwards and the front set points downwards.

5 Glue a small shell to the bird's head to make an eye. Draw a small black circle on the shell to look like the pupil of the eye.

6 Let the glue dry hard, then glue the bird's legs into a flat piece of wood, to make a stand. (Ask an adult to make two holes in the wood for you.)

NATURE GALLERY

Sunflower on a stick

1 Cut a circle out of a thick piece of card. Glue small fir cones over the circle to make the centre of the flower. Leave the glue to dry.

2 Turn the circle of card over. Glue short, straight twigs with large leaves between them to the back of the circle to form the petals.

3 Glue a long, straight stick to the bottom of the card circle. Let the glue dry and set completely before turning the sunflower over.

On display

The models you make will vary depending on the materials you have to hand, but that just makes them more interesting. Use the models here as starting points for your own ideas.

Large evergreen leaf

Short, straight twig

Arrange the fir cones in a pattern on the cardboard.

Long, straight twig stem

Corn dolly

You can dress your corn dolly with any natural materials you can find. Look for things like seedheads, twigs, bark, and dried flowers.

Hat made from small leaves

Raffia arm

Raffia belt holding the dress in place

Dress of evergreen leaves

Sunflower on a stick

When the evergreen leaves begin to droop, replace them with more leaves or with petals made of yellow card.

Fir-cone mice

1 Glue two small pieces of sea glass or shells to the front of the cone under the open end. These are feet for the cones to balance on.

2 Cut two small ears out of pink paper and fold them in the middle. Glue them in place near the top of the fir cone for ears.

3 Glue on two tiny pieces of sea glass for eyes below the ears. Cut short pieces of raffia for the tail and whiskers, and glue them in place.

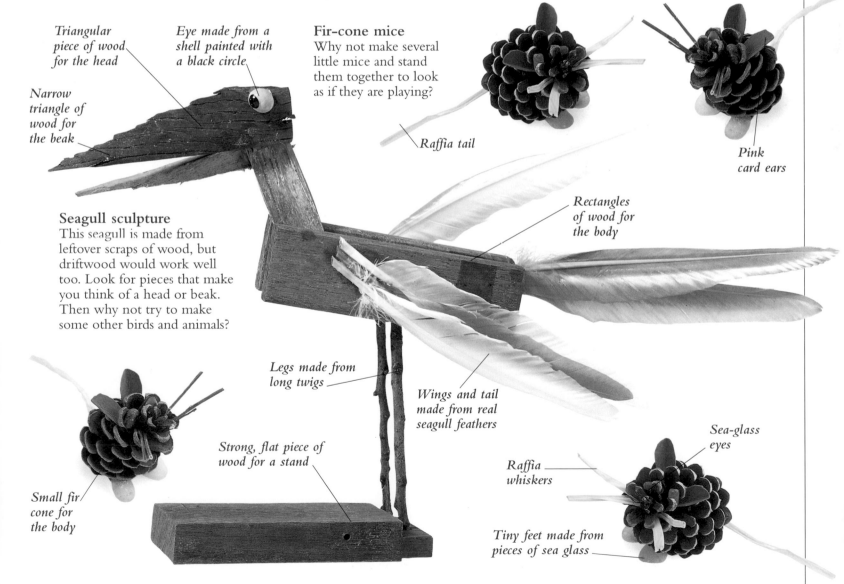

Triangular piece of wood for the head

Eye made from a shell painted with a black circle

Fir-cone mice
Why not make several little mice and stand them together to look as if they are playing?

Narrow triangle of wood for the beak

Raffia tail

Pink card ears

Seagull sculpture
This seagull is made from leftover scraps of wood, but driftwood would work well too. Look for pieces that make you think of a head or beak. Then why not try to make some other birds and animals?

Rectangles of wood for the body

Legs made from long twigs

Wings and tail made from real seagull feathers

Sea-glass eyes

Raffia whiskers

Small fir cone for the body

Strong, flat piece of wood for a stand

Tiny feet made from pieces of sea glass

SEASIDE ACCESSORIES

One of the best things about being on holiday by the sea is looking on the beach for unexpected souvenirs: pieces of sea glass, coloured pebbles, unusual shells, bits of fishing string, and small pieces of twisted driftwood. With a little imagination, all these seaside treasures can be transformed into a fun range of natural jewellery and accessories.

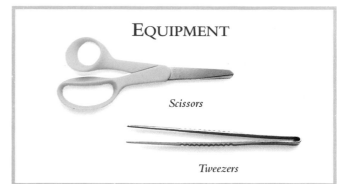

EQUIPMENT

Scissors

Tweezers

You will need

Small shells

Medium and small pieces of sea glass

Large pieces of sea glass

Metal hair slides, brooch backs, rings, and earring backs★

Shells with holes

Rope

Strong glue

String

Making the hair slides

Decorate a hair slide by gluing a row of small shells or sea glass along it. Glue single shells or pieces of sea glass on to rings or earring backs.

Making a brooch

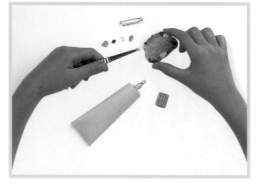

To make a large brooch, glue small pieces of sea glass around the edge of a large piece, using tweezers. Glue the big stone to a brooch back.

Making a necklace

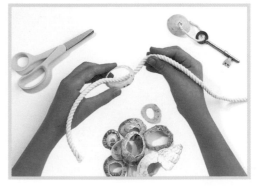

To make a necklace, thread lots of shells on to a length of rope and knot it. For a key ring, thread a key and shell on to some string and knot it.

★Available from large department stores or craft shops.

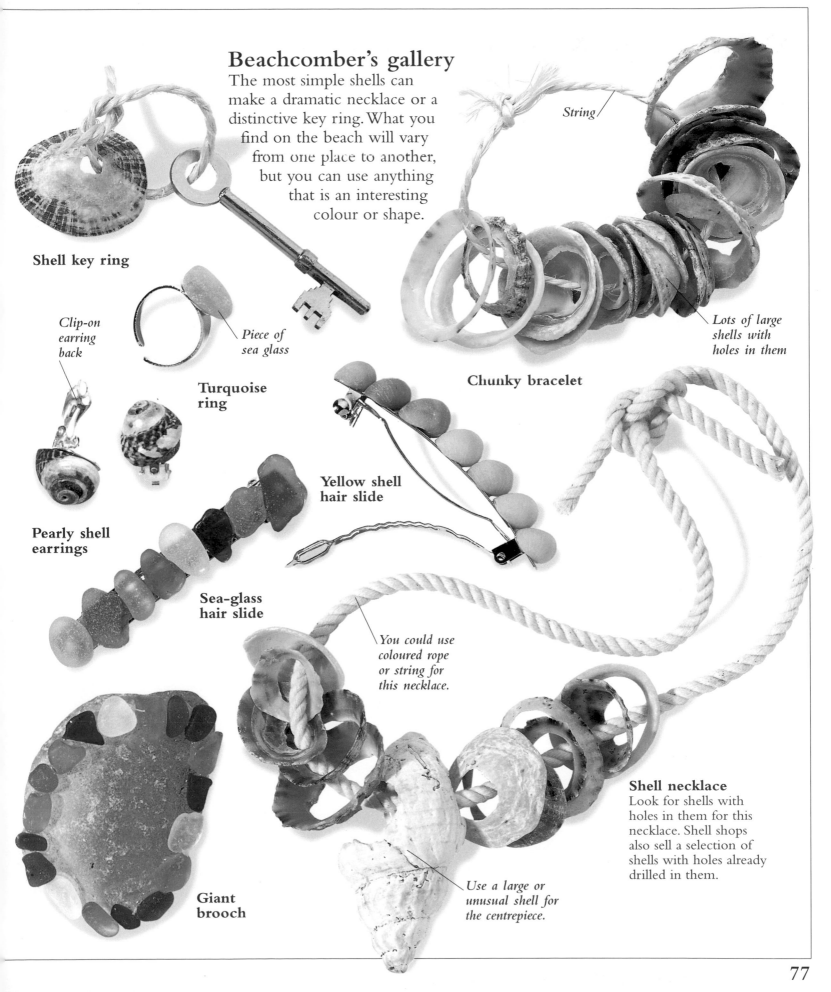

Beachcomber's gallery

The most simple shells can make a dramatic necklace or a distinctive key ring. What you find on the beach will vary from one place to another, but you can use anything that is an interesting colour or shape.

Shell key ring

String

Lots of large shells with holes in them

Chunky bracelet

Clip-on earring back

Piece of sea glass

Turquoise ring

Pearly shell earrings

Yellow shell hair slide

Sea-glass hair slide

You could use coloured rope or string for this necklace.

Giant brooch

Use a large or unusual shell for the centrepiece.

Shell necklace
Look for shells with holes in them for this necklace. Shell shops also sell a selection of shells with holes already drilled in them.

ON THE BEACH

When you are out on walks or on holiday at the seaside, keep your eyes open for interesting objects like oddly shaped pieces of driftwood and sticks, unusual pebbles and shells, leaves, seeds, and other bits and pieces. With a little imagination, you can transform them into all kinds of models and toys. Here you can find ideas for making funny faces, wriggly snakes, boats, and a little cart. Turn the page to see what they look like.

You will need

Seashells

Feathers

Paintbrush

Rounded pieces of sea glass

Modelling clay

Metal staples

Poster paints

Scissors

Strong glue

Hessian

Twigs

String or twine

Evergreen leaves

Interesting sticks and pieces of driftwood

Fir and pine cones

Funny face

Find a flat piece of wood for the face and glue small stones, cones, or shells to it to make the features. You could use feathers or string for the hair.

Wriggly snake

Find a twisted stick and ask an adult to smooth away any rough bits. Then paint on a face and some stripes, to look like a snake's markings.

Seashell coracles

Stick small pieces of modelling clay into some shells. Thread leaves on to small sticks for the sails and push them into the modelling clay.

Jaunty clipper

Mast

1 Ask an adult to make holes in the top of a flat piece of wood. Put sticks in the holes for masts. Add a feather shaft to make the bowsprit.

Rigging   *Cork ring*   *Yardarm*

Mast

Bowsprit

2 Tie small sticks to the masts to make yardarms. Glue a ring of cork to the top of each mast. Tie string to the masts for the rigging.

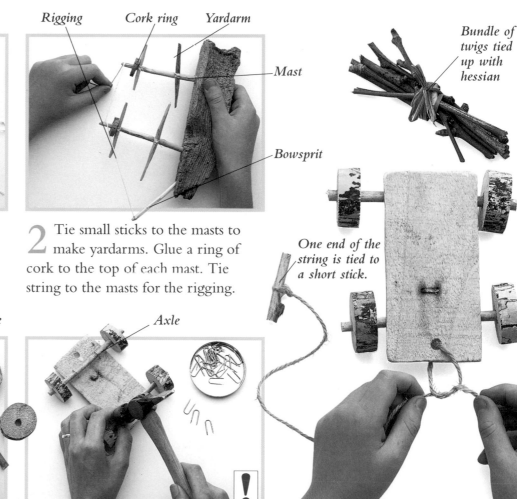

Bundle of twigs tied up with hessian

One end of the string is tied to a short stick.

Caveman's cart

Stick axle

1 To make wheels, ask an adult to saw four slices of wood from a branch and drill a hole in the middle of each. Glue them on to the ends of two sticks.

Axle

2 Find a flat rectangle of wood. Ask an adult to drill a hole in one end. Carefully nail the two axles to the wood with metal staples, as shown.

3 Cut a length of string. Tie one end to a small stick and the other to the cart. Then tie up a bundle of twigs and put it on the cart.

BEACHCOMBER'S GALLERY

Funny faces
These two faces are both stuck on to pieces of driftwood. Try out different things for the features before gluing anything down.

And here are the finished models, together with another face! Why not use them as a starting point for your ideas and design your own models. What you make will vary, depending on the natural materials you have at home.

Paper hat decorated with a feather and a twisted stick

Sea-glass eyes

Shell nose

Shells for earrings

Leaf mouth

Dancing lady

Shell necklace

Thick stick for arms

Feather headdress

Fir-cone eyes

Pebble nose

Mouth made from an old piece of cork

Chief of the forest

Wriggly snakes
Use two or three paint colours for each twisting stick snake and try to keep the pattern regular. Look at pictures of real snakes for inspiration. Paint on eyes and a mouth to add the finishing touches.

Caveman's bundle made from a collection of twigs tied with hessian

Sail made from a leaf

Twig mast

Wooden base

Seashell coracles
Coracles are small, shallow, round boats. Load your coracles with a bounty of sea glass and see how well they float.

Shell boat

Stick axle

Round slices of branch for wheels

Treasure of sea glass and tiny shells

This snake has a smiling face.

String for pulling the cart along

Sails and flags made from scraps of paper

Cork circle crow's nest

Rigging made from fine string

Caveman's cart
You can use your cart to display some of your nature treasures. Then why not try making little cavemen out of sticks and string, to pull the cart along?

You can vary the number of masts and sails you make to suit the piece of wood.

Yardarm made from a short stick

Feather shaft for a bowsprit

Fine thread joints

Jaunty clipper
This driftwood boat would look good on show in your room or decorating the bathroom.

Yellow and green pattern

Old piece of rope for the waves

TINY BOATS

You may know a pond, a bubbling stream, or a rockpool that would be good for sailing model boats. If so, try out your boat-building skills and make a boat that really sails in the wind. Below you can find out how to make a mini-raft and a colourful catamaran from bits and pieces you can find around your home or garden. Ask an adult to go with you when you play near water.

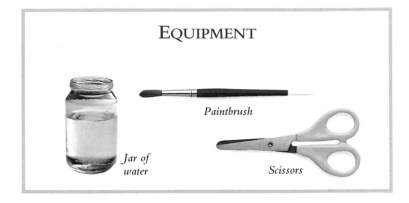

EQUIPMENT

Paintbrush

Jar of water

Scissors

You will need

For the raft

For the catamaran

For sails for both boats

Small, straight sticks about the same length

3 cotton reels

4 champagne or fizzy wine corks

2 bendy plastic drinking straws

Coloured paper

Raffia

Poster paint

Strong glue

Lollipop sticks

Modelling clay

Glue stick

Making the raft

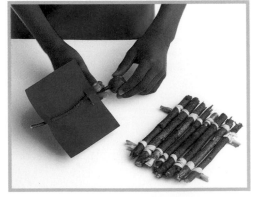

1 Cut out a square of paper for the sail. Cut two slits in the paper, as shown, and thread a stick through them. Glue a paper sun on to the sail.

2 Put eight sticks of the same length next to each other and lay a stick across each end. Tie the sticks tightly together with pieces of raffia.

3 Push one end of the stick mast into a lump of modelling clay. Then push the modelling clay firmly in place on the middle of the raft.

Making the catamaran

1 Cut out a triangle of paper for the sail and make a slit in each corner. Push two straws into a cotton reel and thread them on to the sail, as shown.

2 Paint three lollipop sticks and let them dry. Then glue them across two cotton reels. Glue the cotton reel and sail to the middle of the sticks.

3 Glue the flat ends of the corks on to the ends of the cotton reels. Then make a flag with the bent end of a straw and push it on to the mast.

Setting sail

Place the boats gently on the water and see how they float. The catamaran will float best if the mast is stuck right in the centre of the lollipop sticks. Turn the boats until the sails catch the wind and see which one goes fastest!

Catamaran
To make the flag, cut off the bendy end of a straw. Trim the end of the straw to a point and bend it over.

Mini-raft
The sail is decorated with a paper sun, like the old Inca rafts.

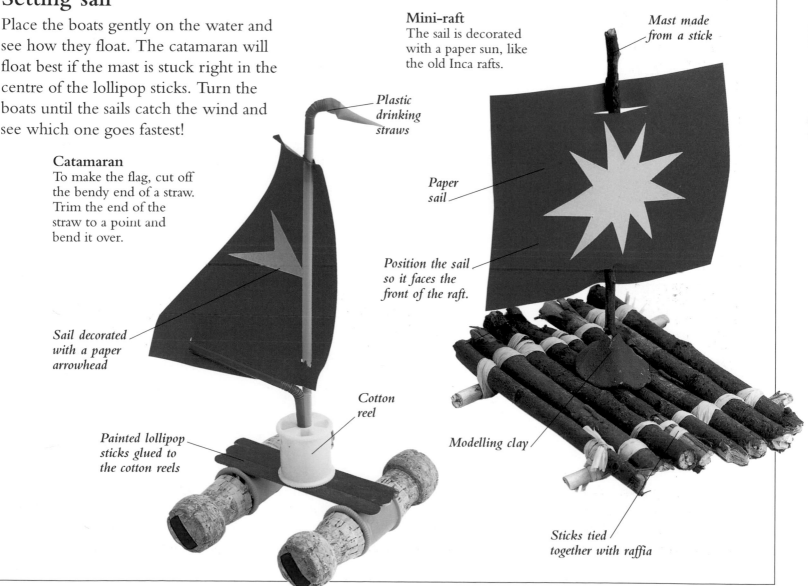

Mast made from a stick

Plastic drinking straws

Paper sail

Position the sail so it faces the front of the raft.

Sail decorated with a paper arrowhead

Cotton reel

Painted lollipop sticks glued to the cotton reels

Modelling clay

Sticks tied together with raffia

ANIMAL TRACKS

You can keep a permanent record of the animal prints that you come across outside by making casts of them from plaster of Paris. If you can't find clear animal prints, why not start by making casts of the hand and footprints that you can make yourself. It is great fun and produces clear casts for your nature museum (see page 94).

EQUIPMENT

Rolling pin

Wooden spoon

Knife

Mixing bowl

You will need

(For one large plaster cast)

Self-hardening modelling clay (for making your own prints★)

420 g plaster of Paris★

Strips of card

Clingfilm

300 ml water

Paperclips

Making a print

1 Lay clingfilm on your worktop. Cut a lump of clay off the block and place it on the clingfilm, then roll it out until it is about 1 cm thick.

2 Press your hand, foot, or shoe firmly down onto the clay to make a clear print, then lift it off again without wriggling.

Making a cast

1 Bend a strip of card into a circle big enough to go around the print. Clip the ends together and push it into the clay around the print.

2 Put the plaster of Paris in the mixing bowl and pour in the water. Mix them with your wooden spoon until smooth and runny.

3 Gently pour the plaster mixture into the card ring until it is about 2.5 cm deep. Leave it for around 15 minutes until the plaster has set hard.

4 Unclip the card and peel it off the plaster. Gently ease the fragile plaster cast away from the clay mould. Leave the cast to set for a day.

Animal casts

You can take casts of animal tracks outdoors in the same way. Simply push a card ring into the mud or sand around each print, and then follow the instructions for making a cast.

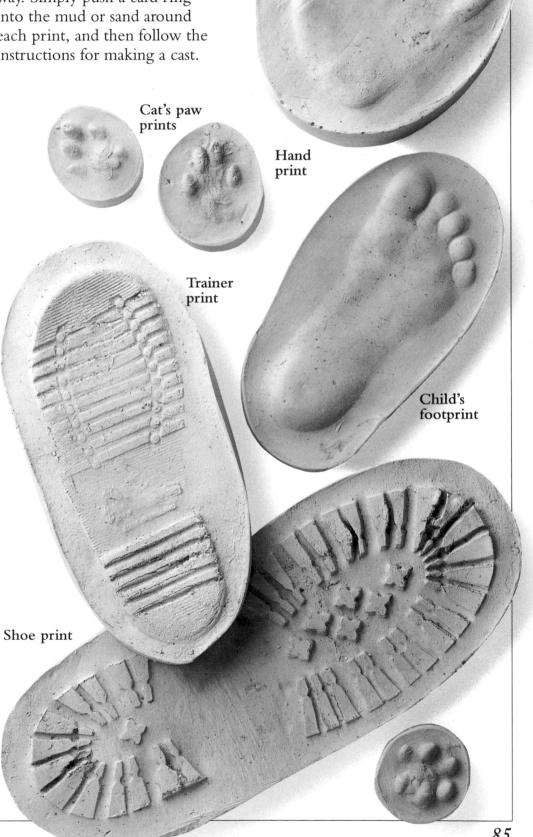

Cat's paw prints

Hand print

Trainer print

Child's footprint

Shoe print

PRESSING PLANTS

Pressed flowers and leaves are beautiful and they last forever. Flowers with flat faces are the easiest to press. Choose dry, undamaged flowers and leaves and press them as quickly as you can, before they start to droop. You can stick them in a nature diary or make them into pictures and cards. Below, you can find out what to do, and over the page are lots of ideas for things to make.

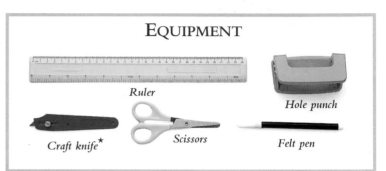

EQUIPMENT

Ruler

Hole punch

Craft knife*

Scissors

Felt pen

Fresh flowers and leaves to press

You will need

A heavy book

Blotting paper

Pansies

Daisies

Welsh Poppy

Purple sage

Parsley

Violas

Columbine

Buttercup

Flat-faced rose

Geranium

Ivy leaves

Periwinkle

Fern

For the nature diary

Corrugated card

Different sorts of paper

Tracing paper

For making pictures

Rubber-based glue

Cotton buds

Thin ribbon

Clear plastic film

Thick paper or thin card

*Ask an adult for help when using a craft knife.

Pressing flowers

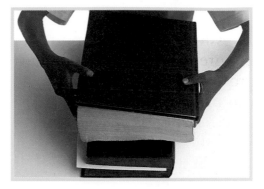

1 Open the heavy book and cut out a piece of blotting paper about the same size as the open pages. Fold the paper in half and then open it out.

2 Lay the paper on the open book. Arrange flowers and leaves flat on the right-hand side of the paper, then fold the left-hand side over the plants.

3 Press more flowers further on in the book. Then stack heavy books on top. Leave the plants to dry for at least four weeks.

Making a nature diary

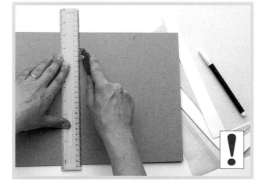

1 Decide what size you want your diary to be. Then ask an adult to cut two pieces of corrugated card to make the front and back covers.

2 Cut out rectangles of paper and tracing paper just smaller than the covers to make pages. Punch holes in both pages and covers, as shown.

3 Put the paper and tracing paper inside the two covers. Line the holes up. Tie ribbons through the holes to hold the book together.

Making pictures

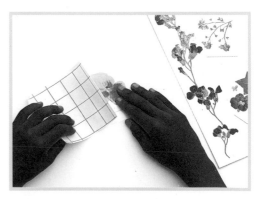

1 Cut out different shaped pieces of white or coloured paper and card. These will be the bases for your cards, pictures, gift tags, and bookmarks.

2 Arrange the flowers and leaves on the paper or card. Then dab a tiny spot of glue on the back of each flower and gently stick it down in position.

3 To protect your cards, cut out a piece of plastic film bigger than the card. Smooth it on to the card. Stick the edges down at the back.

PLANTS ON PAPER

Pressing plants is a wonderful way of keeping a
picture record of all the plants you have seen
growing in your garden. As well as flowers, you
can press leaves, ferns, mosses,
seed heads, and herbs★ and
keep them in a nature
diary or arrange them
into pictures.

*Handle the pressed plants
carefully when gluing them
down as they are very
fragile.*

**Herbal
diary**
You could
use some pages
in your diary to
collect and label
one type of plant,
such as herbs.

*Tracing-
paper sheet*

Nature diary
Your nature diary can be a picture
record of the changing seasons, with
every couple of pages displaying the
plants you collect each month. Even in
winter you will be able to find interesting
things for your diary. Put a page of tracing
paper between each page of plants to stop
them sticking together.

Flower picture

Arrange pressed flowers on a piece of paper, then mount it on a piece of card. Tape a loop of ribbon to the back so that you can hang it up. Arrange the flowers in a pretty pattern or try to make a picture with your pressed flowers and leaves.

Bookmark

Use narrow strips of card to make book marks and cover the flowers with plastic film to protect them.

Nature diary's corrugated card cover

Grey paper mount

Ribbons threaded through a slit in the cover for tying the nature diary shut

Yellow ribbon tie

Gift tags

Glue pressed flowers or leaves to a square of card. Then punch a hole in one corner of each tag and tie a ribbon through it.

Cover the tag with clear plastic film.

NATURE'S PICTURES

Even if you can't draw, you can create wonderful pictures based on things you find outdoors. Here you can learn how to make collages, pressed-flower pictures, bark rubbings, and paintings. Turn the page to see how to finish and frame the pictures.

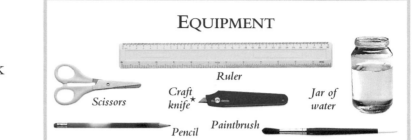

EQUIPMENT

Scissors

Ruler

Craft knife ★

Jar of water

Pencil   Paintbrush

You will need

For pressed-flower and display pictures

Textured paper

A big, heavy book

Blotting paper

Strong glue

Flowers and leaves, or shells and sea glass

For frames

Coloured card

Masking tape

For tree collage

Textured paper

PVA glue   Leaves, twigs, and sticks

For bark rubbings

Masking tape

Wax crayons

Coloured paper

For watercolour painting

Thick paper   Watercolour paints

For tissue-paper collage

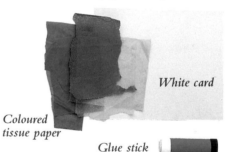

White card

Coloured tissue paper

Glue stick

Pressing flowers

1 Open a big book and lay a sheet of blotting paper over it. Arrange the flowers flat on one half of the paper and fold the other half over them.

2 Press more flowers in the same way, further on in the book. Close it up and stack heavy books on top. Leave it for at least four weeks.

Pressed-flower picture

Arrange the pressed flowers on a sheet of paper. Then dab a tiny spot of glue on the back of each flower and gently stick it down in position.

Seashore picture

You can make a picture from a seashore collection. Arrange your treasures on a sheet of paper. Dab strong glue on the back of each item and stick it down.

Tree collage

1 Stick the paper to card to keep it firm. Glue on a stick for a tree trunk and twigs for branches. Add dead leaves around the bottom.

2 Fill in the rest of the tree with clusters of fresh green leaves to look like the leaves of the tree. You may need quite a lot of glue.

Tissue-paper collage

1 Cut some strips of tissue paper to make the stems of the flowers. Gently glue them to the paper and smooth out any wrinkles.

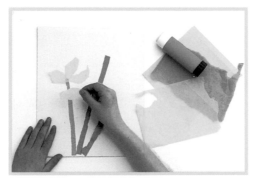

2 Tear petals out of tissue paper in different shades of yellow. Glue some of them down flat and others just at one end, to look ruffled.

Bark rubbings

1 Find a tree with fairly smooth bark and no moss or lichen growing on it. Tape a piece of paper firmly to the tree trunk.

2 Use the flat side of a wax crayon and rub it firmly up and down, to mark the bark pattern on the paper. Then untape the paper.

Flower painting

1 Put the flower you are painting in front of you and draw it as carefully as you can. Keep looking at the real flower to see what it is like.

2 Then paint the flower. Keep to one colour at a time and let each colour dry before painting the next so that they don't run together.

PICTURE GALLERY

Making a frame

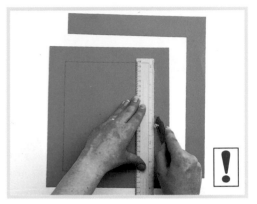

1 Measure the height and width of the picture. Add 3 cm all the way around to give you the size of the outside edges of the frame.

2 Draw the rectangular outer frame on card. Then measure and draw another rectangle inside the first, each side 4 cm smaller than the outer frame.

3 To make the frame, ask an adult to cut along both the inner and outer rectangles for you, using a ruler and a craft knife.

Nature exhibition

Hang the finished pictures up in your room, or beside your nature museum (see over the page). Change your display through the year as the seasons change.

Daffodil pictures
Why not try using different techniques to make pictures of the same subject?

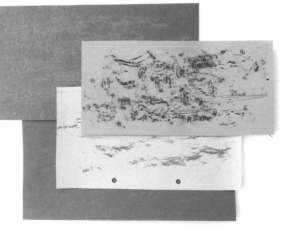

Bark rubbings
Try doing rubbings on different coloured papers, and using chalks as well as wax crayons to create different effects. Write the name of the tree the rubbing comes from on the back of the paper.

The loose petals on this tissue paper collage give the flower a three-dimensional effect.

This picture of a daffodil in a blue jug was painted using watercolour paints.

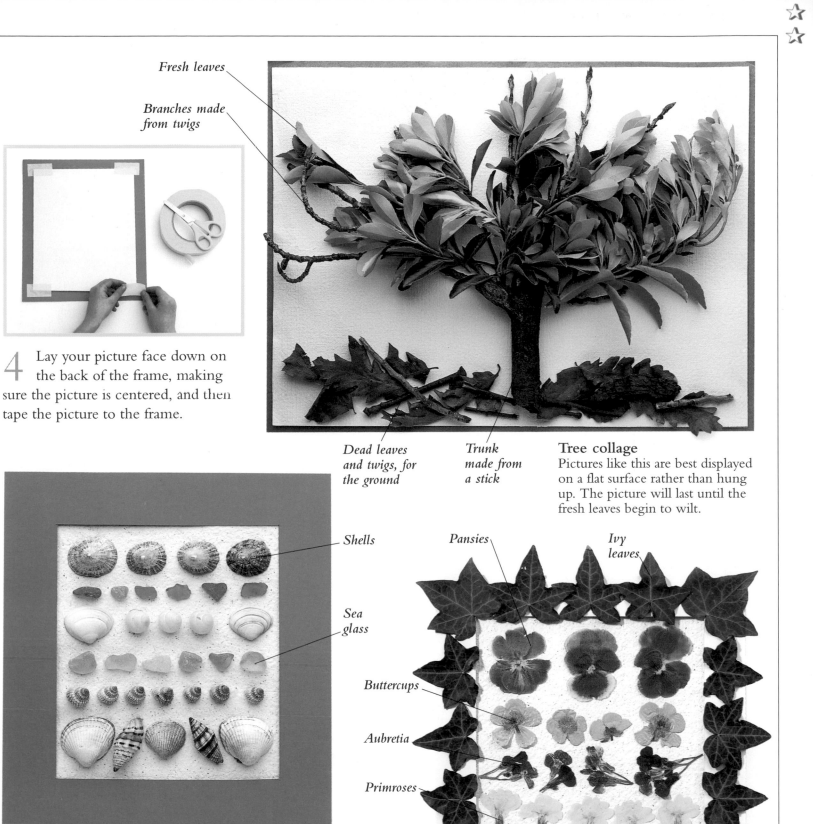

Fresh leaves

Branches made from twigs

4 Lay your picture face down on the back of the frame, making sure the picture is centered, and then tape the picture to the frame.

Dead leaves and twigs, for the ground

Trunk made from a stick

Tree collage
Pictures like this are best displayed on a flat surface rather than hung up. The picture will last until the fresh leaves begin to wilt.

Shells

Sea glass

Shell collages
Collections like this work best if you keep the rows of objects simple and keep similar colours together. You could try arranging your shells into a picture instead.

Pansies

Ivy leaves

Buttercups

Aubretia

Primroses

Pansies

Sampler picture
Arranging the pressed flowers in rows like this makes the picture look like a pretty and traditional needlework sampler.

NATURE MUSEUM

Good nature detectives keep their eyes open for new or interesting finds whenever they are outdoors. Unusual shells, pebbles, leaves, seedheads, stones, and twigs all make good collections to display. Here you can see how to make a tiny chest of drawers and a display showcase for your very own nature museum.

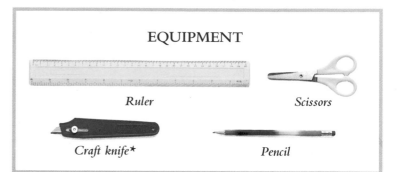

EQUIPMENT

Ruler

Scissors

Craft knife★

Pencil

You will need

For the showcase

For the chest of drawers

Thin, white card for labels

Cotton wool

Thick, coloured card

The insides of 6 large slotted matchboxes, or single matchboxes with small pieces of card glued inside

8 large matchboxes

8 paper fasteners

Green paper

Glue stick

Strong glue

Making the showcase

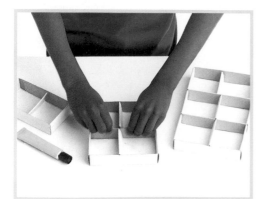

1 Glue three of the matchbox insides together, side by side in a row. Then glue three more box insides together in the same way.

2 Glue the two rows of three boxes together. Fold and glue down the card in the middle of some boxes to make bigger compartments.

3 Ask an adult to cut out a piece of thick card about 3 cm bigger all round than the showcase. Glue the showcase on to the card.

★Ask an adult for help when using a craft knife.

Chest of drawers

1 Glue paper to the front ends of the matchbox insides and push a paper fastener through each one. Fold the card dividers flat inside the boxes.

2 Glue two of the outer boxes together, side by side. Do this with all the outer boxes, then glue the pairs of boxes on top of each other.

3 Cut a strip of paper as wide as the length of the boxes and long enough to wrap right around them. Glue the paper around the boxes.

Treasures on display

The tiny chest of drawers is a good place to keep natural treasures tucked away. Open the drawers a little if you want to display the contents. The showcase is for larger objects that you want to keep on display all the time.

Sea glass in different colours, collected from the beach

Tiny shells

Tiny drawers
These tiny drawers are filled with miniature pebbles, seashells, and pieces of sea glass.

Use the paper fasteners as drawer handles.

Rectangle of green paper glued to the front of the drawer

Showcase
You can use the showcase for any interesting finds, or keep it for one type of collection, such as shells. Arrange the display to look as attractive as possible.

Line the bottom of each compartment with cotton wool.

Make labels from thin card and glue them on.

New finds
Make your museum more interesting by changing the collection from time to time.

OUTDOOR FEAST

What simpler way to cook than to wrap your food in foil and bake it in your camp fire. Use thick baking foil to wrap the food, folding in the edges tightly. Wait until the flames die down, then ask an adult to help you push the parcels into the glowing embers. Here you can find out how to bake potato surprise, apples, and garlic and herb bread in foil. These recipes make one portion.

EQUIPMENT

Chopping board

Cheese grater

Sharp knife★

Apple corer

Teaspoon

Baking foil

Small bowl

You will need

For the potato surprise

1 large potato

Ham cut in cubes

1 chopped tomato

Grated cheese

For the baked apple

1 large dessert apple

A handful of raisins

1 teaspoon brown sugar

A knob of butter

For the garlic and herb bread

1 small French stick

55 g cream cheese

Chives

Parsley

¹/₄ teaspoon salt

1 clove of garlic

Potato surprise

1 Slice a lid off the potato and scoop out the inside with the apple corer. Fill the hollow with chopped ham, tomato, and cheese.

2 Put the lid back on the potato and wrap it in baking foil. Bake it for 1 to 1¹/₂ hours until it is soft in the centre and cooked right through.

Garlic and herb bread

1 Chop the parsley, chives, and garlic. Mix the salt and herbs into the cream cheese and beat it with a spoon until the mixture is soft.

2 Make cuts along the bread and spread the cheese mix inside them. Wrap the foil around the bread and bake it for 15 minutes.

Baked apple

1 Lay the apple on two overlapping squares of baking foil. Core the apple and fill the hole with raisins. Spoon some brown sugar on top.

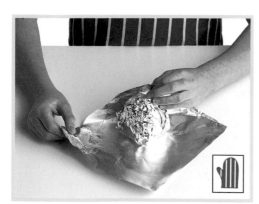

2 Put the knob of butter on top of the sugar and wrap the apple in both layers of foil. Then bake it for 30 to 40 minutes until it is soft.

An outdoor feast

Ask an adult to take the foil parcels out of the fire for you. Let the parcels cool a little and then unwrap them. Test the potato and apple with a sharp knife to make sure they are soft. If not, wrap them up again and put them back in the embers to cook for longer.

Baked apple

Potato surprise

Serve the foil parcels in paper napkins so that people do not burn their fingers.

Use two layers of foil for baked apples to protect the apple skin from burning.

When eating outside, use plastic spoons to eat your potato and apple.

Garlic and herb bread

FIRESIDE COOKING

Food grilled outdoors on a barbecue has a special smoky flavour all of its own. Even the simplest things taste delicious. Here you can find out how to barbecue sausage kebabs and beefburgers. Prepare the food indoors and then take it out to the barbecue to be cooked. Make sure there is an adult there to help you. The recipes here will serve four people.

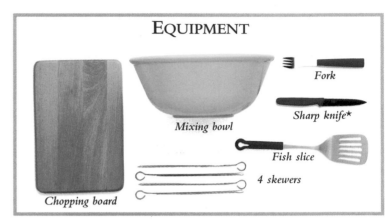

EQUIPMENT

Fork

Sharp knife★

Mixing bowl

Fish slice

4 skewers

Chopping board

You will need

For the kebabs

450 g small sausages

1 red onion

1 courgette

1 red and 1 green pepper

Cherry tomatoes

For the beefburgers

450 g minced beef

4 sesame seed buns

1 egg yolk

Half an onion, finely chopped

Salt and pepper

For garnishing

Sliced cheese

Sliced tomato

Sliced cucumber

Lettuce

Making the kebabs

1 Remove the cores and pith from the peppers and cut them into squares. Slice the courgette in rounds and cut the peeled onion into quarters.

2 Thread the chopped vegetables and sausages on to the skewers as shown. Be very careful with the sharp points on the skewers.

3 Ask an adult to check when the barbecue is ready. Then grill the kebabs for 10 to 15 minutes, turning them so that they cook all over.

★Ask an adult for help when using a sharp knife.

Making the beefburgers

1   Put the minced beef, egg yolk, finely chopped onion, and salt and pepper into the mixing bowl. Mix them together well with one hand.

2   Split the mixture into four even-sized parts. Roll each one into a ball, then flatten it and firm round the edges to make a circular beefburger.

3   When the barbecue is hot, put the beefburgers on the grill and cook them for 5 to 10 minutes on each side until they are firm and brown.

The open–air grill

You can eat the kebabs straight away. Pick up the skewers carefully as they will be hot, then slide the sausages and vegetables off on to your plate using a fork. Assemble the beefburgers as below for a real feast!

Turn the skewers so the kebabs cook all over.

All in a bun
Arrange each beefburger in a bun with a slice of cheese, tomato, cucumber, and some crisp lettuce.

Other kebabs
You can vary your kebabs by using cubes of chicken or lamb, or adding small mushrooms.

SUMMER COOLERS

What's better on a hot summer's day than a cool, refreshing drink? Here are three tasty recipes for you to try. The sunset punch and fruit cooler can be made in minutes and they both make enough for two people. The fresh lemonade needs to be prepared one day in advance before drinking. This recipe makes enough for four thirsty people.

EQUIPMENT

Chopping board

Sieve

Large bowl

Potato peeler

Large spoon

Sharp knife*

Juice squeezer

Measuring jug

Blender

Jug

You will need

For fresh lemonade

750 ml boiling water

For sunset punch

225 ml apricot juice

For fruit cooler

140 g strawberries

1 banana

3 large lemons

75 g caster sugar

150 ml pineapple juice

150 ml orange juice

Wedge of lemon

1 small pot natural yoghurt

225 ml milk

15 g (1 tablespoon) caster sugar

Fresh lemonade

1 Wash the lemons. With the peeler remove the peel from two lemons into a bowl. Trim off any white pieces of pith you find on the peel.

2 Cut all three lemons in half and squeeze their juice into the bowl. Add the sugar, then carefully stir in the boiling water.

3 Leave the lemonade in a cool place overnight. Then strain the mixture through a sieve into a jug, ready to serve.

Fruit cooler

Sunset punch

1 Peel the banana. Slice and put it into the blender. Squeeze a little lemon juice on top. Wash the strawberries and chop off the stalks.

2 Put the yoghurt into the blender with the bananas, strawberries, milk, and sugar. Blend for about a minute, until frothy. Serve into a glass.

Pour the orange juice, pineapple juice, and apricot juice into a jug and mix them together well with a large spoon. Chill before serving.

Fruity refreshers
Pour the drinks into tall glasses. Add ice cubes made from fruit juice or with pieces of fruit set into them, and serve with sliced fruit and coloured drinking straws.

Sunset punch

Add ice cubes made from cranberry juice, for a sunset glow.

Novelty drinking straw

Fresh lemonade

Fruit cooler

Strawberry slotted on to the edge of the glass

Half a strawberry frozen into an ice cube

Cut a slit to the middle of each orange and lemon slice and slot them on to the glass.

MAKING SWEETS

What better way to spend the afternoon than to make some delicious sweets for everyone to enjoy? Here you can see everything you need to make peppermint creams, pink sugar mice, and marzipan bonbons. Then turn the page to see a mouthwatering array of the finished sweets.

EQUIPMENT

For marzipan sweets

Wooden spoon

Sharp knife★

Sieve

Fork

Sweet cutters

Mixing bowl

Small bowl

Rolling pin

For peppermint creams

Fork

Whisk

Sieve

Wooden spoon

Sharp knife★

Small saucepan

Baking sheet lined with non-stick silicone paper

Mixing bowl

Small bowl

You will need

For marzipan sweets

115 g icing sugar

225 g ground almonds

Pink food colouring

115 g caster sugar

Green food colouring

1 egg   An extra egg yolk

3 drops vanilla essence

Liquorice strings   Glacé cherries

1 teaspoon lemon juice

For chocolate peppermint creams and sugar mice (makes 16 creams and 4 mice)

55 g dark chocolate

1 egg white

Pink food colouring

340 g icing sugar   Currants

A few drops peppermint essence

4 shelled peanuts

Liquorice strings

Making the peppermint mixture

1 Put the egg white in the mixing bowl and beat it lightly with the whisk until it looks frothy but has not yet gone stiff.

2 Sift the icing sugar into the bowl. Then stir it into the beaten egg white with a wooden spoon until the mixture is stiff.

3 Add a few drops of peppermint essence and knead it into the mixture. The more essence you add, the stronger the mints will taste.

Chocolate peppermint creams

4 Split half the mixture into 16 balls and put them on the lined baking sheet. Press them flat with a fork and leave them to set for 24 hours.

5 When the creams have set, break the chocolate into the small bowl. Set the bowl over a pan of simmering water until the chocolate melts.

6 Dip each peppermint cream into the melted chocolate, then put them back on the baking sheet until the chocolate has set hard.

Sugar mice

1 Knead a few drops of pink food colouring into the other half of the peppermint mixture, then break it into four even-sized pieces.

2 Shape each piece of the pink mixture into an oval shape with your hands, then pinch one end of each oval to make a pointed snout.

3 Add two currants to each oval to make eyes and peanut halves to make ears. Cut small pieces of liquorice string to make the tails.

Making the marzipan

1 Sift the icing sugar into the mixing bowl to remove any lumps. Then add the caster sugar and the ground almonds and stir them together.

2 Mix the egg, egg yolk, lemon juice, and vanilla essence together in the small bowl. Add them to the sugar mixture and mix them in.

3 Gently knead the mixture with your hands until it becomes a smooth, thick paste. Add a little more icing sugar if the mixture is sticky.

CANDY DISPLAY

Marzipan colours

Split the marzipan into three balls. Leave one ball plain. Add a little pink colouring to one ball and green to the other. Knead until the colour is even.

Roly-poly sweets

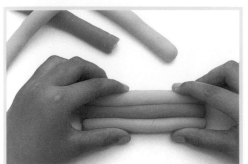

1 Roll some plain marzipan into a small sausage. Roll out the same amount of green and pink marzipan and cut each into a rectangle.

2 Roll the green and then the pink rectangles around the sausage. Then trim the ends and slice off small rounds, to make the finished sweets.

Checkerboard sweets

1 Cut six equal pieces of marzipan, two of each colour. Roll them into long sausages, then press three different coloured sausages together.

2 Press the remaining sausages on top, making sure that no sausage is next to a sausage of the same colour. Flatten the sides, and cut into slices.

Cut-out sweets

Roll out some marzipan until it is about 0.5 cm thick. Cut out shapes, such as butterflies and flowers, with the sweet cutters.

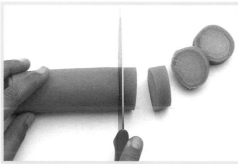

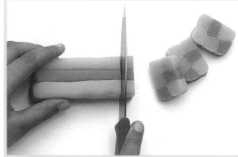

Sweet treats

Arrange the finished sweets in a pretty pattern on a big plate or tray. Below is a guide to all the different types of sweets.

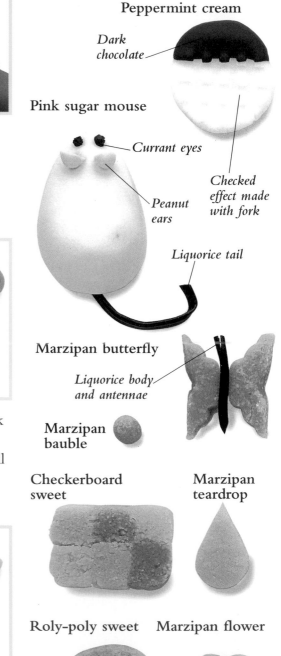

Peppermint cream

Dark chocolate

Checked effect made with fork

Pink sugar mouse

Currant eyes

Peanut ears

Liquorice tail

Marzipan butterfly

Liquorice body and antennae

Marzipan bauble

Checkerboard sweet

Marzipan teardrop

Roly-poly sweet

Marzipan flower

Three rings of coloured marzipan

Piece of glacé cherry

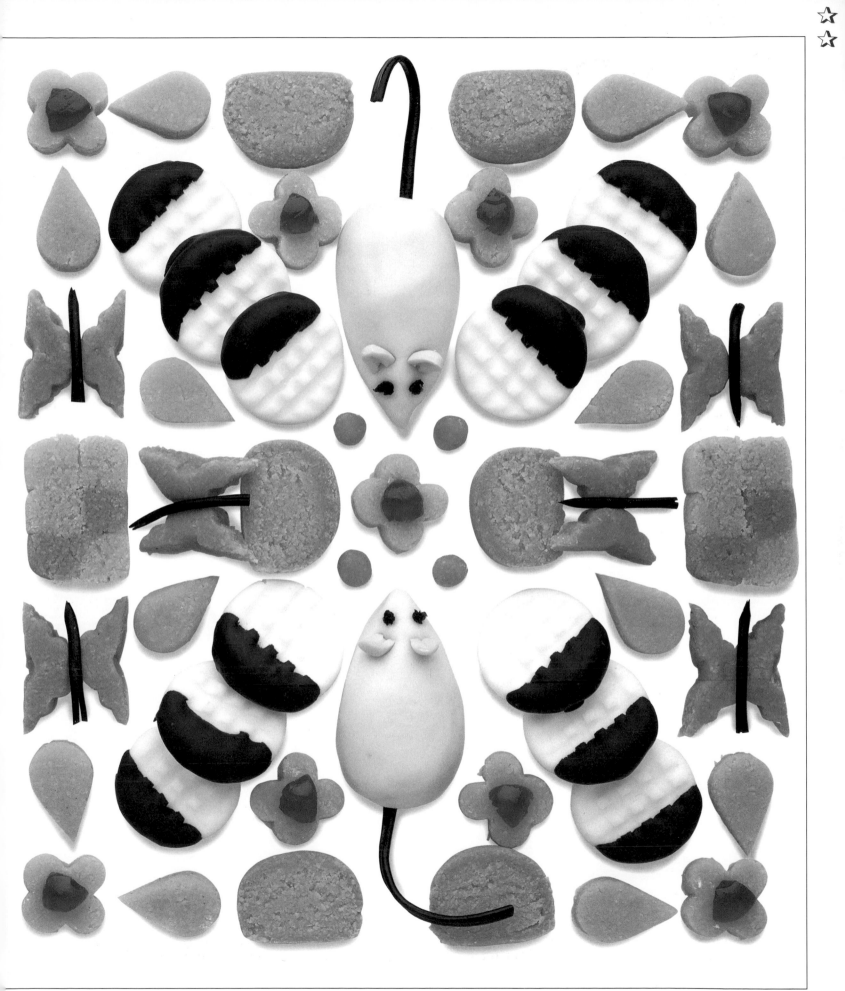

MUFFIN BONANZA

American muffins are quick to make and taste delicious still warm from the oven. Try one of the three versions shown here: white chocolate and strawberry, orange and poppyseed, or apple and cinnamon. Alternatively, you could add your own ingredients to the basic recipe. The quantities given here make 12 muffins.

EQUIPMENT

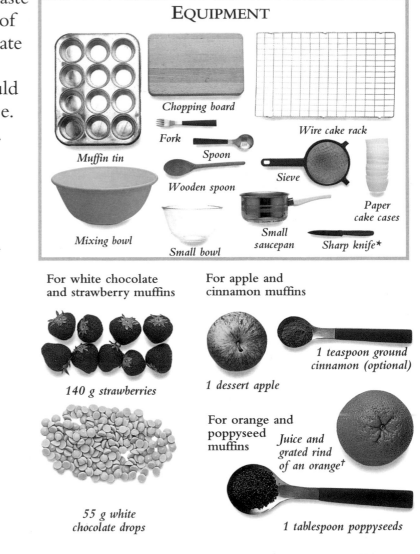

Chopping board

Fork

Spoon

Wire cake rack

Muffin tin

Wooden spoon

Sieve

Mixing bowl

Small bowl

Small saucepan

Paper cake cases

Sharp knife★

You will need

For the basic mixture

240 ml milk

85 g soft brown sugar

2 eggs

1 level tablespoon baking powder

A big pinch of salt

55 g butter

285 g plain flour

For white chocolate and strawberry muffins

140 g strawberries

55 g white chocolate drops

For apple and cinnamon muffins

1 dessert apple

1 teaspoon ground cinnamon (optional)

For orange and poppyseed muffins

Juice and grated rind of an orange†

1 tablespoon poppyseeds

What to do

1 Put the paper cases in the muffin tin. Set the oven to 200°C/400°F /Gas Mark 6. Melt the butter in the saucepan, then let it cool a little.

2 Sift the flour, baking powder, salt, sugar (and ground cinnamon, if you are using it) into the mixing bowl and stir everything together.

3 Beat the eggs in the small bowl. Pour in the milk (and orange juice and rind, if you are using it) and whisk together. Stir in the melted butter.

★*Ask an adult for help when using a sharp knife.*
†*The juice and grated rind of an orange can replace 120 ml of the milk.*

4 Peel and chop the apple (or the strawberries) into small pieces. Add them and the rest of the ingredients to the bowl of flour. Add the egg mixture.

5 Beat all the ingredients together, then spoon the mixture into the muffin cases. Put them into the oven to bake for about 25 to 30 minutes.

6 The muffins are cooked when they have risen and are firm and golden brown. Move them carefully on to a wire rack to cool.

Tempting treats

Muffins taste best eaten warm from the oven on the day they are made. However, if you have any left uneaten, put them in an airtight tin and keep this in a cool place or in the freezer. They will stay fresh for several days.

Apple and cinnamon muffin

Orange and poppy seed muffin

Strawberry and white chocolate muffin

Pretty doily
For a special occasion decorate your plates with pretty paper doilies. Take a 30 cm square of greaseproof paper and fold it in half, twice. Then using scissors, cut a rounded edge opposite the point. Cut small shapes in the paper to make a pattern. Unfold it and you have a delicate doily.

PAINTED FACES

You can have great fun with your friends by painting each other's faces. You can become a tiger, a clown, or anything you like! Look for pictures in books and magazines for ideas, and then copy the details when you paint. The best face paints are water-based ones, which are easy to apply and quick to wash off afterwards. You can blend face colours together to make new shades, just as you do with watercolour paints.

You will need

Face flannel

Cosmetic sponge

Hair band

Water-based face paints

Tubes of glitter for faces

Jar of water

Thin paintbrush

Broader, flat paintbrush

Applying a base

Put a hair band on your model. Wet the sponge and squeeze it out so it is just damp. Rub it gently in the base colour and then sponge the paint evenly over the face.

Adding the detail

Allow the base colour to dry. Then paint on details, using the face paints like normal paints. Use the flat brush for large areas of colour and the thin brush for details.

Cleaning up

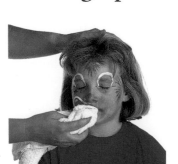

Wipe off the face paints with soap and water and a clean face flannel. Don't let soap get in the eyes.

Happy clown

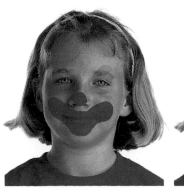

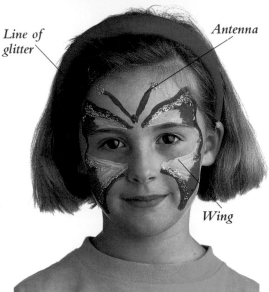

The hair has been gelled and tied back.

Orange starburst

Purple star

Add lines around the eyes.

1 This face doesn't need a base. Paint two green ovals over the eyelids and eyebrows.

2 Then paint on a large, red mouth and a red circle on the end of the nose.

3 Paint white outlines round the eyes and mouth, and add white highlights where shown.

Butterfly face

Line of glitter

Antenna

Wing

1 With the thin brush, paint on the outline of the butterfly's wings and antennae.

2 Then paint in the patches of colour inside the wing outline with the flat brush.

3 Paint smaller areas of colour with the thin brush. Add lines of glitter paint where shown.

Terrible tiger

Thick black and white tiger stripes

Thin black whiskers

White fluffy muzzle

1 Sponge on yellow around the middle of the face and orange around the edges.

2 When it is dry, paint on feathery white eyes and a muzzle, and fan them out at the edges.

3 Paint a black mouth and nose. Add black lines round the eyes and spots on the muzzle.

JUNK JEWELLERY

You don't need gold and precious gems to make fabulous jewellery. You can create stunning necklaces, bracelets, and earrings, with paper and a few colourful bits and pieces. Look around your home for buttons, beads, shiny sweet wrappers, and ribbons, then add sequins and glitter for extra sparkle.

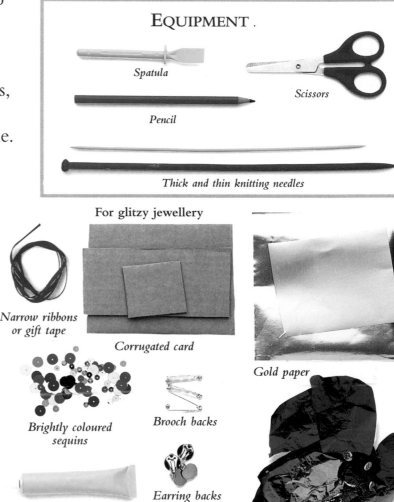

EQUIPMENT

Spatula

Scissors

Pencil

Thick and thin knitting needles

You will need

For rolled-paper jewellery

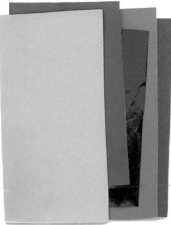

Coloured paper in different thicknesses

Magazine pages

For glitzy jewellery

Narrow ribbons or gift tape

Corrugated card

Gold paper

Brightly coloured sequins

Brooch backs

Small, wooden beads

Glue stick

PVA glue

Earring backs

Scraps of coloured foil and sweet papers

Rolled-paper jewellery

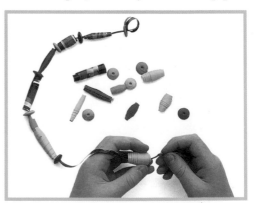

1 Cut out lots of long thin triangles from magazine pages and coloured paper, as shown. The triangles should be about 30 cm long.

2 Spread glue on the thinnest two thirds of each triangle. Then, starting with the wide end, roll up the triangle round a knitting needle.

3 When you have enough paper beads, thread them on to some ribbon with a wooden bead between each one and tie the ribbon together.

Glitzy jewellery

1 Draw heart shapes and diamonds on corrugated card and cut them out. Cut the same shapes out of gold paper and glue them on to the card.

2 Tear up small pieces of coloured foil and sweet papers and glue them all over the gold shapes. Then glue sequins on top of the foil.

3 Make small holes in the gold shapes and thread them on to thin ribbon to make necklaces, or glue them on to earring and brooch backs.

Colourful collection

Rainbow-bright and sparkling, the finished jewellery is great fun to wear and makes wonderful presents, too. Experiment with different shapes, designs, and colours for glitzy jewellery, and with different textures of paper for rolled-paper beads.

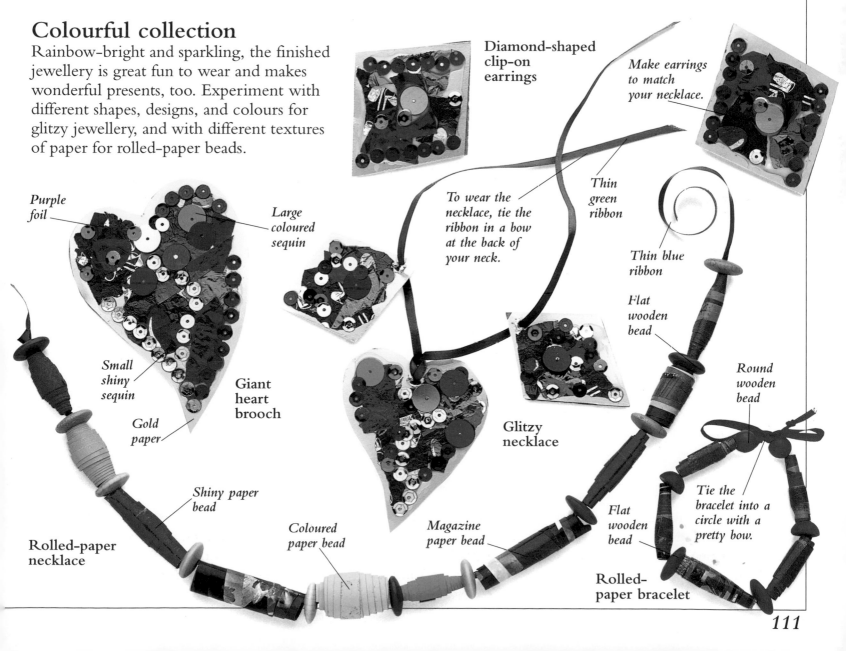

Diamond-shaped clip-on earrings

Make earrings to match your necklace.

Purple foil

Large coloured sequin

To wear the necklace, tie the ribbon in a bow at the back of your neck.

Thin green ribbon

Thin blue ribbon

Flat wooden bead

Round wooden bead

Small shiny sequin

Giant heart brooch

Gold paper

Glitzy necklace

Shiny paper bead

Coloured paper bead

Magazine paper bead

Flat wooden bead

Tie the bracelet into a circle with a pretty bow.

Rolled-paper necklace

Rolled-paper bracelet

111

SHINING JEWELS

You can add some sparkle to any costume with this glittering range of jewellery. If you can't buy the gemstones shown below, make your own from small, round sweets covered with silver, gold, or coloured foil. Save the foil wrappers from chocolate bars and sweets.

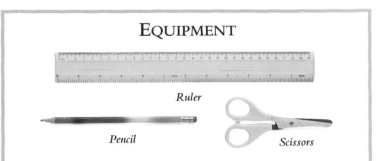

EQUIPMENT

Ruler

Pencil

Scissors

You will need

Corrugated card

Gold and silver foil

Thick string

Gold braid★

PVA glue and spatula

Flat-backed glass gemstones★

Thin wire for necklaces

Sticky tape

Garden cane for wand

Making the jewels

1 Draw the jewellery shapes you want to make on corrugated card, using household objects as templates. Then cut them out.

2 For big jewels, such as a star for a wand or a medallion, cut out two large stars or circles and glue them together, to make them stronger.

3 Spread glue over the card shapes and stick pieces of string to them in circles or tight spirals. Put the shapes to one side until the glue dries.

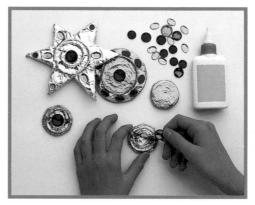

4 Cover each shape with foil, folding it to the back and gluing it down. Press the foil over the string so the pattern shows through.

5 Glue glass gemstones to the shapes for decoration. Use a large gem in the centre of big shapes and glue smaller gems around the edges.

6 For a necklace, cut pieces of thin wire and bend them into loops. Tape a loop to the back of each jewel and thread the braid through the loops.

Glittering collection

You can use your jewels in endless different ways: thread them on to braid to make regal necklaces, belts, and medallions; glue them to earring or brooch backs; or attach them to plain rings for a sparkling transformation.

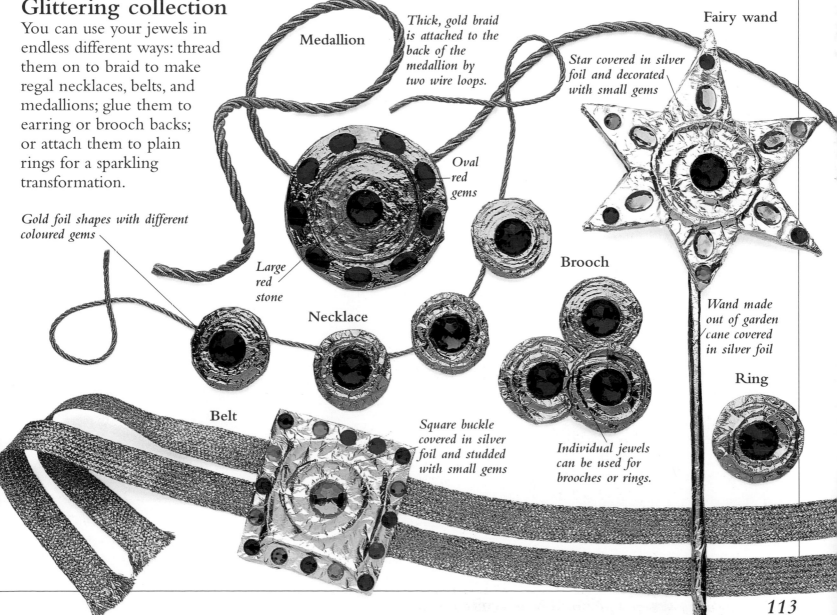

Medallion

Thick, gold braid is attached to the back of the medallion by two wire loops.

Fairy wand

Star covered in silver foil and decorated with small gems

Oval red gems

Gold foil shapes with different coloured gems

Large red stone

Brooch

Necklace

Wand made out of garden cane covered in silver foil

Belt

Ring

Square buckle covered in silver foil and studded with small gems

Individual jewels can be used for brooches or rings.

TOP TO TOE

With a little imagination, you can transform ordinary straw hats, baseball caps, and canvas shoes into personalised works of art which are fun to decorate as well as wear. Gather together colourful beads, buttons, and other odds and ends before you start.

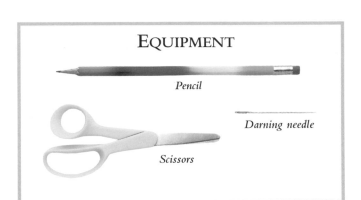
You will need

For the cap

For the shoes

For the sunhat

Baseball cap

Strong glue

Plain canvas shoes

Straw sunhat

Sticky tape

Plastic bag ties

Coloured buttons

Coloured buttons

Washers

Coloured beads

Tubes of all-purpose fabric paint*

Coloured tissue paper

Straw sunhat

1 Cut large and small flowers out of red and purple tissue paper. Roll up strips of purple tissue. Secure with tape and snip a fringe.

2 Glue together several flower shapes. Thread a button on a bag tie and twist the end to secure it. Pull the tie through a purple roll.

3 Push a tie through the centre of a flower. Thread the needle with the tie and attach it to the crown of the hat. Bend the tie back, to secure it.

*Available from large department stores or craft shops.

Canvas shoes

Stepping out

Copy these decorative ideas or experiment with your own. For example, you could try covering a straw hat or canvas shoes with buttons and a baseball cap with fabric paints.

Bright yellow laces add a splash of colour.

Wavy water line

Nautical shoes
These canvas shoes have a seaside theme, with pictures of a boat, anchor, and life buoy.

Remove the laces from the shoes. Using one colour, paint shapes and pictures on the shoes and leave to dry. Use another colour to fill in the shapes.

Baseball cap

Glue buttons, beads, and washers to the cap in a pattern. Stick smaller buttons and beads on top of larger ones to add more detail.

Button caps
Use brightly coloured beads and buttons in as many different shapes as you can find to decorate your cap and create patterns.

Fish-shaped buttons

Wavy piece of braid

Buttons attached to the brim

Washer and bead on top of a button

Fringed purple tissue paper with a button in the centre

Purple flowers made in the same way as the red flowers

Red flower petals

Floral sunhat
Fasten three large red flowers to the front of the hat, and smaller, purple flowers around the crown.

MAKING HATS

Hats come in all shapes and sizes and are great fun to dress up in. Put on a hat and you can pretend to be anyone you like. Here you can find out how to make three great hats from thin card and a few extras. You will need to measure your head with a band of card before you make the top hat and the boater.

EQUIPMENT

Jar of water

Ruler

Paintbrush

Sticky tape

String

Pencil

Scissors

You will need

Thin black, white, and yellow card

Poster paints

Green, yellow, pink, and blue tissue paper

Green ribbon

Silky scarf

Measuring your head

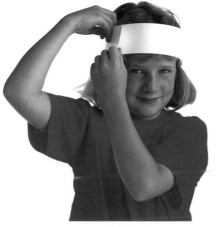

Cut a narrow strip of card and wrap it round your head. Tape down the overlapping edge. This band shows the size of your head.

2 Cut a long length of card about 16 cm tall. Roll it to fit inside the brim and tape it in place on the inside. Tape the overlapping edges.

Making a top hat

1 Tape the band to some black card. Draw round inside it then draw a circle 5 cm out from the band. Take off the band and cut out both circles.

Making a boater

Make a boater 7.5 cm tall out of white card, as for the top hat. Tape the circle cut from inside the brim to the bottom of the hat. Then paint the hat.

Making a sunhat

1 To make the brim draw one circle, as shown on page 234, 17 cm across and a second circle 42 cm across around it. Cut out both circles.

2 Fold a sheet of tissue paper in half and gently push it into the hole, as shown. Trim off the rough edges and tape the tissue paper inside the brim.

3 Tape a scarf across the tissue paper, as shown. Scrunch squares of tissue paper into flowers and tape them around the brim of the hat.

Hat parade

Here are all the featured hats, ready to wear. Try making other styles, like a witch's hat, a crown, or even a huge sombrero, to complete your dressing-up wardrobe.

Jolly boater

Hat painted with broad yellow, red, and blue stripes

Top hat

Stick a band of shiny ribbon around the hat to hide the paper join.

Flowers made from scrunched-up tissue paper

Flowery sunhat

Tissue paper crown

Tuck a colourful card under the ribbon to add a touch of colour.

Tie the hat under your chin with the silky scarf.

Yellow card brim

QUICK DISGUISES

With a little imagination, and bits and pieces from your scraps box, you can put together a quick disguise and turn yourself into another person. You could be a detective, a famous movie star, or even Father Christmas. Change your clothes and put on a hat and no-one will know who you really are.

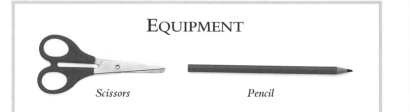

EQUIPMENT

Scissors   Pencil

You will need

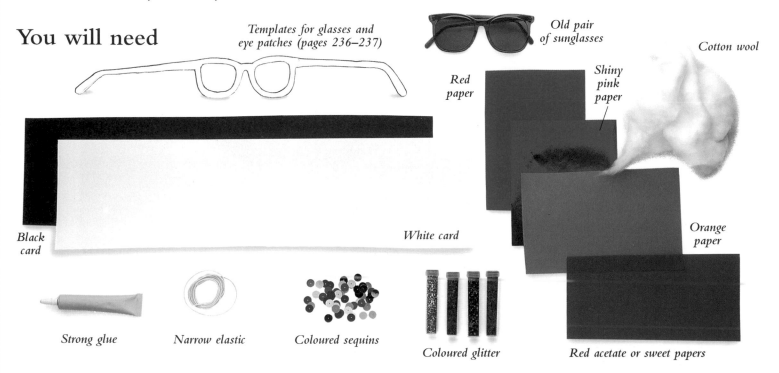

Templates for glasses and eye patches (pages 236–237)

Old pair of sunglasses

Cotton wool

Shiny pink paper

Red paper

Black card

White card

Orange paper

Strong glue

Narrow elastic

Coloured sequins

Coloured glitter

Red acetate or sweet papers

False noses

1 Make noses out of coloured paper. Cut out a kite shape long enough to cover your nose and fold it in half. Give the nose big, round nostrils.

2 Cut a piece of elastic long enough to go round the back of your head. Thread it through two holes at the top of the nose and knot the ends.

Eye patches

Using the template on page 237, draw an eye patch on card and cut it out. Glue on glitter, if you like. Attach a length of elastic, as for the nose.

Detective disguise

Movie-star shades

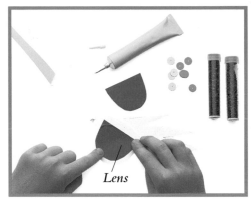

Instant disguise

Using the template on page 236, draw and cut out glasses from black card. Glue a false nose on to the glasses and a black card moustache on to the nose.

Use the glasses with wings template to make shades. Glue lenses cut out of acetate to the back of the shades. Decorate the front with glitter.

Lens

Draw a beard and moustache on white card and cut it out. Glue bits of cotton wool all over it. Tie some elastic to the sides of the moustache, as for the nose.

Disguise kit

Here are the finished disguises. They are all really quick and easy to make. You can wear each one on its own or combine two or three with a hat from page 117 for a total disguise.

False nose

Detective disguise

Wicked moustache

False nose

Instant disguise

Old sunglasses

Movie-star shades

Sequin

Glitter frames

Acetate lens

Cotton wool

Pirate's eye patch

Glittery eye patch

Shiny false nose

Father Christmas's beard

119

HAIRY DISGUISES

For a complete change of face, why not make yourself a bushy beard and bristling moustache? Or hide your own hair under a hat and grow some chunky plaits? Here you can make both these hairy disguises, as well as a useful collection of false moustaches.

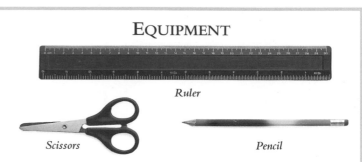

EQUIPMENT

Ruler

Scissors

Pencil

You will need

For the plaits

Hat

Wire *Safety pins*

Ball of wool *Ribbon*

For the beard and moustache

Ball of wool

PVA glue *Thin, white card* *Narrow elastic*

For card moustaches

Thin, black card

Card moustache

Fold the black card in half. Draw half a moustache shape, as shown, next to the fold. Cut out the shape and then open out the moustache.

2 Cut pieces of wool twice the length you want the beard. Loop 3 pieces of wool at a time around the lower part of the mouth piece and tie.

Woolly beard

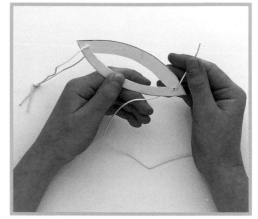

1 Cut out a mouth piece, as shown. Make a small hole at each side, then thread a piece of elastic through each hole and tie it into a loop.

3 For the moustache, cut shorter lengths of wool. Lay them across the top of the mouth piece and tie them in place with a piece of wool.

Chunky plaits

1 Cut 40 pieces of wool the length you want each plait to be. Split the wool into three bunches. Tie them firmly together at one end, as s...

2 Plait the wool, starting from where it is tied together. Tie the other end of the plait tightly, to stop it from unravelling.

3 Thread some wire through each plait. Pin the finished ends inside the hat with a safety pin. Tie bows around the other ends of the plaits.

Cover-ups

You can add other features, such as a hat, specs, or scarf, to complete your disguise. Turn to page 158 for more costume ideas to wear with the moustaches, beards, and plaits.

Long, pointed moustache

Curly moustache

Adapt the nose clip to fit your nose.

Small moustache

Moustaches
The moustaches vary in shape but are all made from black card.

Wire in the plait makes it bend into funny shapes.

Chunky plaits
By using different coloured wool or other hats you can create a whole new costume.

Elastic loops

Gingham bow

Woolly beard
Hook the loops of elastic around your ears to keep the bushy beard and moustache in place.

MAKING MASKS

Why not make a mask for a fancy-dress party, for a special play, or just for dressing up? All the masks here cover your face to provide a complete disguise, and they are made from nothing more than paper plates and torn paper. Try copying the ideas shown here, or make up some masks of your own.

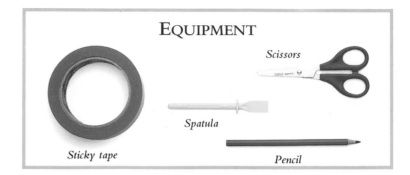

EQUIPMENT

Scissors

Spatula

Sticky tape

Pencil

You will need

Large white paper plates

Coloured paper

Coloured tissue paper

Rubber-based glue

Tubes of glitter

White crêpe paper

White plastic beakers

Thin elastic

Pages torn from old magazines

Red-eyed frog

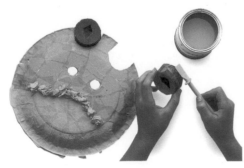

Cover a plate with green and yellow tissue paper. Cut two holes for nostrils. Make the eyes from the ends of two beakers covered with tissue paper.

Harlequin mask

Tear up diamonds of pink, yellow, and blue tissue paper and glue them on to the plate. Cut two diamonds for eyes and stick on a black paper mouth.

Leo lion

Cover a plate in torn yellow and orange magazine paper. Use strips of brown tissue paper for a mane and make the features of the face out of paper.

Polar bear

Cut off the end of a beaker. Tape it into a hole the same size cut in the centre of a paper plate. Then glue balls of white crêpe paper over the plate and beaker.

Red-eyed frog

Stand-out beaker eyes

Green tissue face

The nostrils are the eye holes of the mask.

Scrunched paper mouth

Mask collection

Here are all the finished masks. When you aren't wearing your masks, you can hang them up by the elastic on your bedroom walls.

Harlequin mask

Torn tissue diamonds

Black paper mouth

Bird of paradise

Make a beak from two folded triangles of yellow paper and stick them to a plate. Make a face with pink paper and glitter and feathers from tissue paper.

Leo lion

Torn tissue paper mane

White paper whiskers

Black paper features

Polar bear

Adding the elastic

Make a hole at each side of the mask. Cut some elastic long enough to go round your head and thread it though the holes. Tie a knot in each end.

Black paper features

Muzzle made from a paper covered beaker.

Bird of paradise

Glitter

Torn tissue crest

Blue tissue feathers

Yellow card eyes

Folded yellow card beak

Ears made of card covered in pink paper and white crêpe paper balls.

123

BOX MASKS

Here and overleaf you can find out how to make amazing lion, bird, and insect masks out of cardboard boxes. For each mask you will need a strong, light box that fits over your head as far as your shoulders. Below, you can see how to make it fit properly so it doesn't slip when you wear it. Save interesting pieces of packaging to create features for the masks.

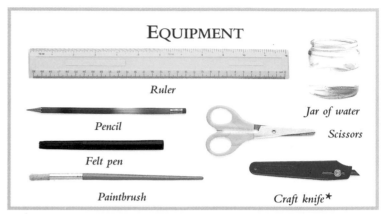

EQUIPMENT

Ruler

Jar of water

Pencil

Scissors

Felt pen

Paintbrush

Craft knife ★

You will need

Strong glue

Glue stick

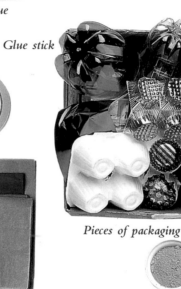

Masking tape

Coloured paper

Sticky tape

Coloured tissue paper

Pieces of packaging

Paint

Cardboard boxes

The basic box mask

1 Cut the flaps off the box (keep one flap for the lion mask). If the box is too long from front to back, cut it in half, as shown.

2 Slide one half of the box over the other until the box fits your head. Firmly tape the two halves together where they overlap.

3 Try the box on and feel where the eye holes should be. Take the box off, mark the spots with a pencil and cut out two holes for your eyes.

Wild lion

1 Leave one flap on the box. Cover the flap and front of the box, half of the top and sides with yellow paper, folding it and gluing it in place.

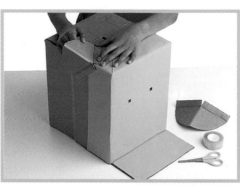

2 Cut two ears out of cardboard and fold them in half. At the base of the ears bend back tabs and tape them to the top edges of the box.

3 Tear up some short and long strips of orange and brown paper. Glue them to the front flap, top, and sides of the box, to make a mane.

4 Tear out pieces of coloured paper to make a nose strip, nose, eyes, and whiskers. Glue them to the box and then draw on a mouth.

Exotic bird

1 Cover the back, top, and sides of a box with blue paper. Draw a bird's crest on thick card, cut it out and cover it with yellow paper.

2 Make short cuts every 3 cm along the bottom of the crest. Fold them back to make tabs and tape them to the top of the box.

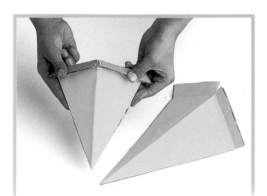

3 For a beak, cut out two triangles of card, one longer than the other. Cover them with yellow paper and fold in half. Bend tabs at the ends.

4 Tape the beak tabs to the box. Gather several pieces of blue and lilac tissue paper and tear out feather shapes.

5 Glue the paper feathers to the box, working forwards from the blue paper. Glue two circles of pink tissue paper around the eye holes.

MASQUERADE

Evil insect

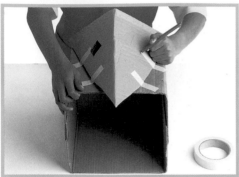  

1 Cut three triangular corners of varying sizes off a box. Tape the largest one to the front of the mask. Cut two holes in it over the eye holes.

2 Tape a corner to the top of the box and the last corner on the back. This corner may need a ball of modelling clay, to act as a weight.

3 Stick pieces of plastic packaging over each eye hole and cut a hole in them. Paint the whole mask with thick green paint and let it dry.

Wild lion

The mane for the lion mask is built up by gluing on long strips of paper, then gluing shorter strips just below the face.

Evil insect

You can vary the insect mask depending on the pieces of packaging you have at home. Anything black or shiny will do. You could even try painting the mask blue or black instead.

Nose strip and other features torn out of coloured paper

Mouth drawn on with a thick black pen

Feelers made from strips of shiny green card with foil cup cases taped to the end

Glue torn strips of black paper around the mouth for whiskers

Birds and beasts

With a little imagination, each mask can be the basis for a whole costume. Turn to page 158 for some more ideas.

4 Cut out circles of green foil and stick them on to the box. Glue the base of a green plastic bottle to the top of the insect's face.

5 Cut three long strips of shiny card. Slot them through slits in the mask and tape them in place. Decorate the face with foil cup cases.

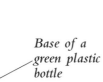

Circle of shiny green foil

Base of a green plastic bottle

Exotic bird
Choose any colours you like for the bird's feathers. You could make it look like a parrot by using red, blue, and yellow feathers. Or leave out the crest and make white feathers, to create a duck.

Crest made of card covered in yellow paper

Feathers torn out of blue and lilac tissue paper

Eyes made from plastic packaging with foil cup cases stuck on top

Rings of dark pink tissue paper for eyes

Proboscis made from a strip of shiny green card

Blue circles drawn on beak for nose holes

Beak made from card covered in yellow paper

DECORATING T-SHIRTS

You can transform plain T-shirts with amazing designs by painting, printing, stencilling, or tie-dying them. Use white or light-coloured T-shirts for the best results and choose fabric paints in strong, contrasting colours. It is a good idea to draw a clear design for each T-shirt before you start. Turn the page to see what great works of art you can produce in an afternoon.

EQUIPMENT

Sharp knife ★

Thick paintbrush

Thin paintbrush

Saucer

Biscuit cutter

Glass of water

Pencil

Scissors

Felt pen

Craft knife ★

Large bowl

Rubber gloves

You will need

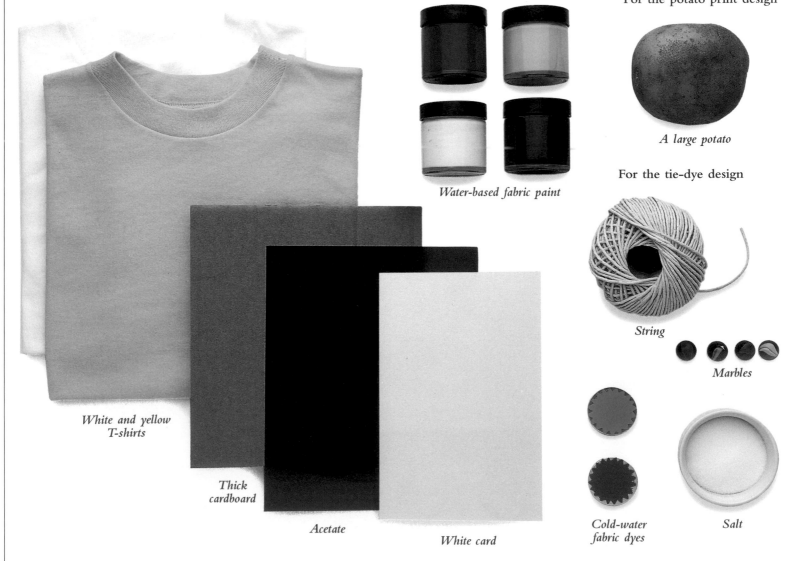

White and yellow T-shirts

Thick cardboard

Acetate

White card

Water-based fabric paint

For the potato print design

A large potato

For the tie-dye design

String

Marbles

Cold-water fabric dyes

Salt

Stencilled T-shirt

1 Draw shapes for stencils on the acetate. Lay the acetate on thick card and ask an adult to cut the stencils out with a craft knife.

2 Lay a stencil flat on the T-shirt. Decide which colour paint to use, then dab it all over the cut-out stencil with a paintbrush.

3 Carefully lift the stencil off the T-shirt, so you do not smudge the paint. Continue using other stencils and different colours. Leave to dry.

Hand-painted T-shirt

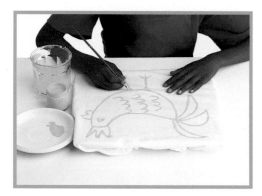

1 Draw a design on some white card to the size you want for your T-shirt. Use a dark pen and keep the design bold and simple.

2 Slip the card inside the T-shirt so the design is where you want it. Paint over the outline of the design in a light-coloured fabric paint.

3 Paint in the main colour of the design and let it dry. Then add the details in other colours, keeping the paint as thick as you can.

Potato-print T-shirt

1 Slice a potato in half. Press a star-shaped biscuit cutter into each half of the potato. Then carefully cut away the potato around the cutter.

2 Mix some thick paint in a saucer. Cover the potato star with a thick coat of paint, then firmly press it down in position on the T-shirt.

3 Lift the potato off carefully. Use the other half of the potato to print another colour. Repaint the potatoes each time you use them.

T-SHIRTS ON SHOW

The finished T-shirts are bold and colourful. Let the paint or dye on each T-shirt dry and then ask an adult to help you iron them. You can copy the designs shown here, or try experimenting with pictures and patterns of your own.

Tie-dyed T-shirts

1 To make a stripy T-shirt, roll up a white T-shirt tightly. Tie long pieces of string securely around the T-shirt at 10 cm intervals.

2 For a circular design, tie a marble in the middle of the T-shirt's front and in each sleeve. Tie string at 5 cm intervals from each marble.

A white T-shirt tie-dyed in red with marbles and string creates a circular effect.

Red and yellow star-shaped potato prints

An all over design with hand-painted sunflowers

Circular T-shirt

Starry T-shirt

Sunflower T-shirt

3 Wearing rubber gloves, mix the cold-water dye in a bowl. Follow the instructions on the packet and add the salt. Soak the T-shirt in the dye.

4 After one hour, take the T-shirt out of the dye and wring it well. Rinse the T-shirt under cold water until the water runs clean.

5 Very carefully cut the string tied around the T-shirt and remove all the ties and marbles. Hang the T-shirt up to dry, then iron it.

Large hand-painted picture

A white T-shirt tie-dyed in blue with string, creates these stripes.

Stencilled fish and seashells around the top and bottom

Cockerel T-shirt

Stripy T-shirt

Seaside T-shirt

SWIRLING SKIRTS

You don't need to be a whiz with a needle and thread to make your own costumes. Here you can find out how to make a stunning range of grass skirts using coloured crêpe paper. You can follow the ideas on this page or design your own variations.

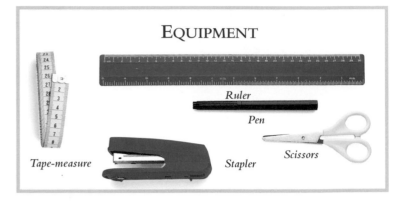

EQUIPMENT

Tape-measure
Ruler
Pen
Stapler
Scissors

You will need

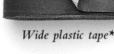
Glue stick

Sticky tape

Nylon fastener★

Wide plastic tape★

Coloured crêpe paper

Basic grass skirt

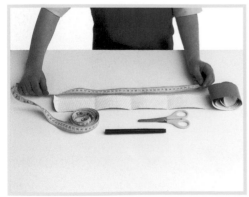

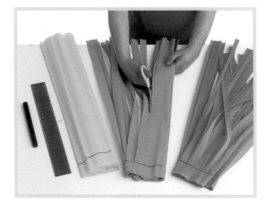

1 Measure around your waist with the tape-measure and add 60 mm to this measurement. Cut some wide plastic tape to the same length.

2 Cut three pieces of crêpe paper the same length as the tape. Fold and cut them, as shown, into thin strips, stopping 25 mm from the top.

3 Stick each piece of paper in layers to the lower half of the tape and fold the top half of the tape back down over them.

Ra-ra skirt

Rags-and-tatters skirt

4 Cover the tape with crêpe paper and decorate it with paper shapes. Staple nylon fasteners to each end of the skirt to fasten it around you.

Make this in the same way as the grass skirt, but shorter. Attach to the tape seven or more layers of crêpe paper cut to different lengths.

Follow the basic grass skirt steps. Use five pieces of different coloured crêpe paper for this skirt, cutting the skirt strips into points.

Dancing skirts

Choose contrasting colours for your skirt to make a dramatic outfit. Turn to page 158 to see how to use these skirts as part of a costume.

Waistband decorated with triangles of crêpe paper.

Ra-ra skirt
Layered crêpe paper gives this skirt a ruffled appearance.

Grass skirt
This skirt is made up of layers of yellow, orange, and green crêpe paper.

Rags-and-tatters skirt
To make this skirt look ragged, cut the crêpe paper into pointed strips.

TUNICS

A tunic is a very useful basis for any costume. Although it is simple to make, it can be dressed up by adding belts, scarves, jewellery, or anything else you have around the house. Here, you can see how to make a royal tunic and a forest archer tunic without doing any sewing at all. You can use any type of fabric and vary your costume with colours and patterns.

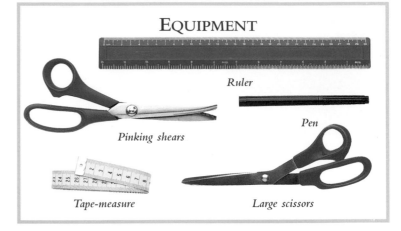

EQUIPMENT

Ruler

Pinking shears

Pen

Tape-measure

Large scissors

You will need

For the archer tunic

140 cm x 70 cm fabric for each tunic

Pouch made from circle of fabric tied with braid

Narrow scarf or tie belt

For the royal tunic

Medallion
(see page 113)

Necklace or chain
(see page 113)

Wide gold ribbon
or braid

Royal tunic

1 Lay the fabric out flat on a table or the floor, smoothing out any wrinkles. Measure out a piece 140 cm long and 70 cm wide and cut it out.

2 Fold the fabric in half lengthwise. Measure 15 cm in from each edge on the fold. Cut a slit between the two marks to make a neck hole.

3 Using the pinking shears, trim all along the outer edges of the tunic. This will help to stop the fabric from fraying.

Archer tunic

1 Follow steps 1 and 2 for the royal tunic. Then cut a slit 15 cm long in the centre front of the neck to make the collar flaps.

2 Draw deep points along the bottom edges of the tunic, using a ruler and pen. Cut along the lines you have drawn to make a ragged edge.

Tunic outfits

These two tunics can be worn over T-shirts, or on their own. Tie a scarf, ribbon, or braid belt around your waist or hips and add other decorations to fit the character you are playing. You can vary the basic tunic by making it in different fabrics, or by cutting out a larger piece of material and turning it into a dress.

Archer tunic
Make this tunic in a woodland colour, such as green or brown. The lower edge of the tunic is cut into points to make it look ragged.

T-shirt

Pouch fastened with braid

Collar flaps folded back at neck

Narrow scarf tied at the front

Bottom of tunic cut into points

Necklace or chain with jewels

Royal tunic
Use heavy, silky fabric in a regal colour, like red, purple, or gold, and add plenty of gold and jewels.

Wide gold ribbon tied around waist

Medallion

Heavy red curtain fabric

135

UNDER WRAPS

There are some costumes that are very simple to make and can be invented by playing around with whatever odd bits of fabric you have: old towels, curtains, or tablecloths.★ You wrap, twist, tug, and tie and instantly you are a Roman emperor or a desert island dancer! Big safety pins are handy for these costumes and ribbons, jewellery, and flowers are great accessories.

EQUIPMENT

Pinking shears

Tape-measure

Scissors

Crêpe paper flower in hair

You will need

For a sarong

A piece of flowery fabric about 90 cm x 170 cm

The skirt needs to be pulled tightly around your waist.

Material tied at the back of the neck

Narrow piece of fabric

Tie the fabric in a knot at the side.

Smaller piece of same fabric about 170 cm x 30 cm

Crêpe paper flower

Sarong
Place the narrow piece of fabric around your back. Then cross the ends of the fabric over your chest and tie them behind your neck. Wrap the large piece of fabric around your waist and tie the ends together at the side.

Arrange the fabric so that it falls in folds.

Start wrapping

Here you can see how to make an exotic sarong, a Roman toga, and a regal turban. All of the costumes are simply made by wrapping pieces of fabric around your body and fastening them in place.

You will need

For a Roman toga

Safety pins

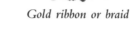

Brooch and belt (see page 113)

Gold ribbon or braid

2 large white towels

You will need

For a turban

A long piece of silky fabric

Brooch (see page 113)

Roman toga

Wrap one towel tightly around your waist like a skirt. Tuck in the ends and pin them securely. Drape the second towel over one shoulder and tuck the front into the skirt.

Gather the towel in with braid and fasten on a brooch

Tie a belt, ribbon, or braid around your waist.

Towel tucked into belt at the back

Paper scroll

Towel folds over at the front

Twist the ends of the fabric together tightly, as shown.

Turban

Wrap the fabric around your head with the ends in front. Twist the ends together flip them back over the turban and tuck them in at the back of your head.

Decorate the front of the turban with a brooch.

CLOAKS AND CAPES

Swirling cloaks and capes are an important addition to many costumes. Kings, queens, witches, wizards, and even birds and insects are enhanced by dramatic cloaks. Here we show you two easy methods for making the cloaks, one for royal robes and the other for a fluttering cape. Turn the page for more ideas.

EQUIPMENT

Stapler

Black pen

Scissors

Safety pin   Needle

Tape-measure

Pinking shears   Pins

You will need

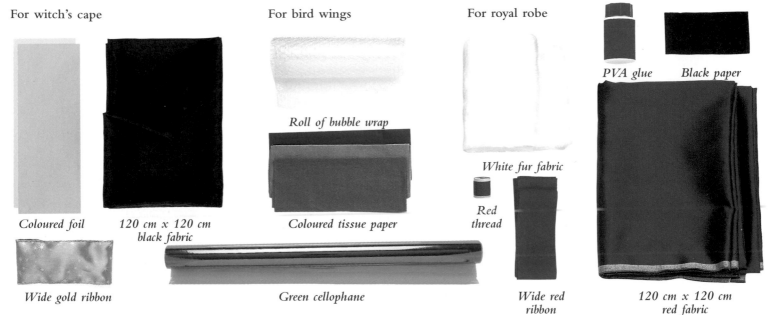

For witch's cape

Coloured foil

120 cm x 120 cm black fabric

Wide gold ribbon

For bird wings

Roll of bubble wrap

Coloured tissue paper

Green cellophane

For royal robe

PVA glue   Black paper

White fur fabric

Red thread

Wide red ribbon

120 cm x 120 cm red fabric

Bird wings

1 Tape a sheet of bubble wrap together to make a sheet 160 cm x 80 cm. Fold it into a square. Cut a neck hole and trim the bottom edge.

2 Draw and cut out points along the bottom edge of the cape. Cut two strips of bubble wrap for ties and staple one to each side of the neck.

3 Gather together coloured pieces of tissue paper. Carefully tear out lots of feather shapes. You will need both large and small feathers.

4 Tape the larger feathers on to the cape in rows. Pinch each feather in the middle as you tape it down, to make it stick out a little.

5 Tape over the staples joining the neck ties, to cover any sharp ends. Then decorate the neck edge with the smaller feathers.

6 Cut two long narrow strips of bubble wrap. Bend them into loops and staple to each side of the cape, to make loops for your wrists.

Royal robe

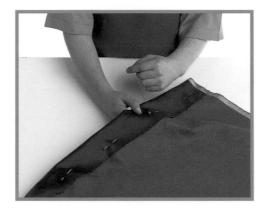

1 Trim the red fabric. Fold one edge of the fabric, 6 cm wide, over to the back side and pin it in place. This is the casing for the ribbon.

2 Thread a needle with a double thread and knot it at the end. Sew firmly along the bottom edge of the folded fabric, as shown★.

3 With pinking shears, cut strips of fur fabric 6 cm wide. Use these pieces of fur fabric to decorate the sides and bottom edges of the robe.

4 Dab glue along the back of each fur strip. Glue the strips of fur on to the front of the robe, down the sides, and along the bottom edges.

5 Cut out lots of small rectangles of black paper. Carefully glue them all over the fur fabric on the robe, as shown.

6 Thread a long ribbon through the folded casing at the top of the robe with a safety pin. Gather the fabric as you pull it through.

★Turn to page 235 for sewing tips. 139

CAPE COLLECTION

You can create your own costume by using different materials and unusual decorations to adapt the cloaks and capes shown here.

Feathers torn out of different coloured tissue paper

Pointed edges cut into the bubble wrap

Wrist loop

Bird wings
Fasten the ties loosely around your neck and slip your hands through the wrist loops. Lift your arms and flap your wings!

Insect cape
This cape is made in the same way as the bird's wings, but uses crinkly green cellophane instead.

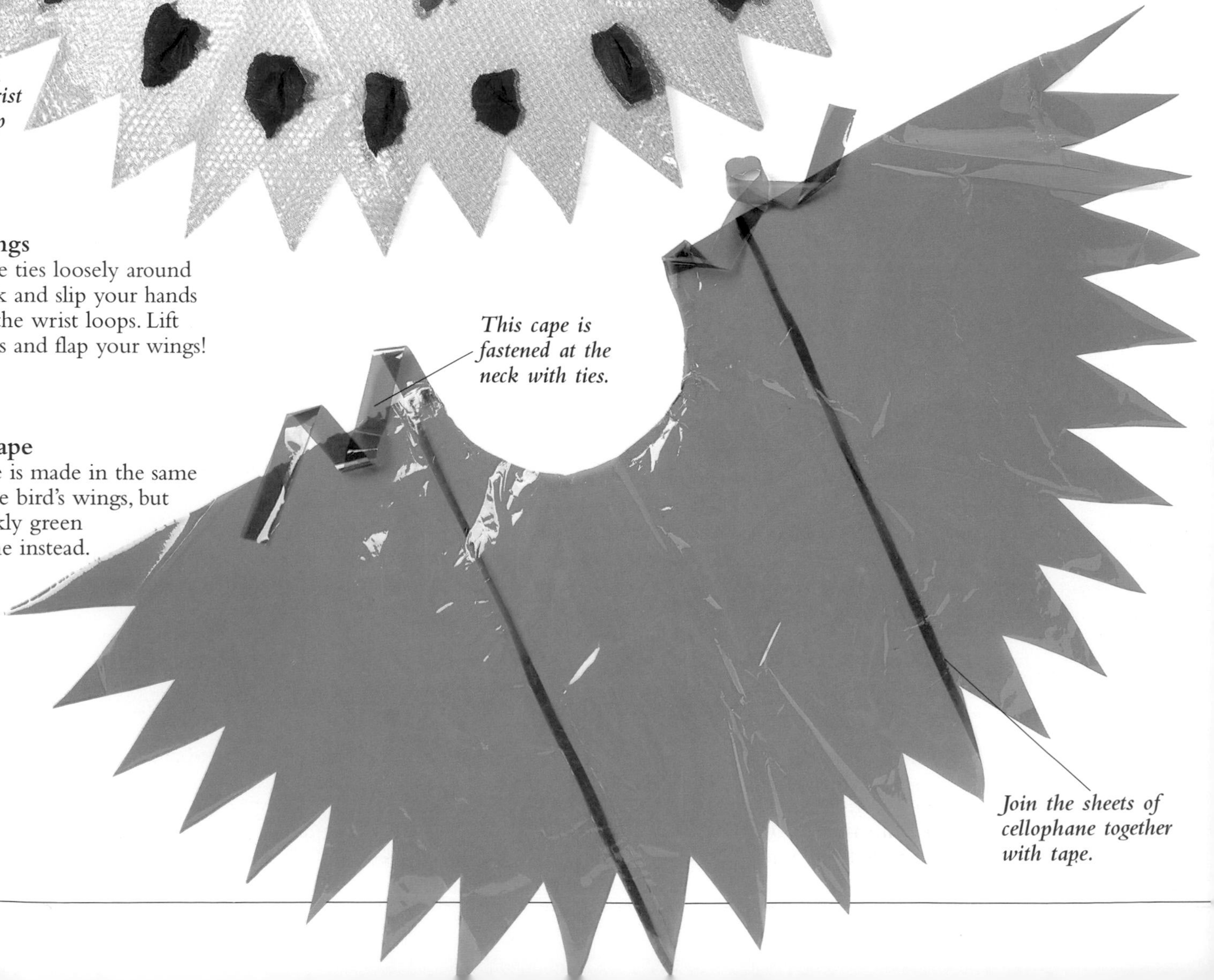

This cape is fastened at the neck with ties.

Join the sheets of cellophane together with tape.

140

Tie the neck ties in a loose bow.

Finishing touches

Here are just a few ways to make your cloaks and capes. To make a wizard's cape, try using blue material and green stars. Turn to the Costume Parade on page 158 for more ideas on what to wear with the wings and robes.

Broad ribbon gathers the cloak in at the neck.

Royal robe

Choose a dark red or purple fabric for this cloak to give it a truly royal appearance.

Trim made from white fur fabric and pieces of black paper

Stars made from coloured foil

Witch's cape

To make this cape, follow the pattern for the regal robe but use black material instead. Decorate it with silver and gold stars cut from foil and a gold ribbon.

141

PANTOMIME HORSE

For a fancy dress party, why not make your own pantomime horse costume that you wear with a friend? The horse is made in two pieces: a box mask for the head and a fabric body. You can use fur fabric for the body, or perhaps an old blanket or towel.* Turn the page to find out how to put your costume together and how to move around in your finished horse.

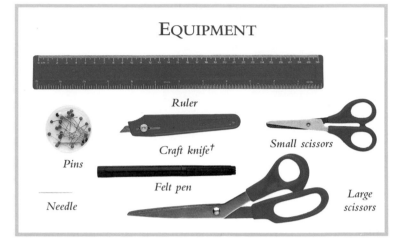

EQUIPMENT

Ruler

Craft knife†

Small scissors

Pins

Felt pen

Needle

Large scissors

You will need

3 sheets of brown paper

Brown fur fabric
240 cm x 80 cm

Glue stick

Reel of brown thread

Black paper

Sticky tape

2 boxes the same size, each big enough to fit over your head

2 sheets of black crêpe paper

Dark brown, yellow, and white paper

Making the head

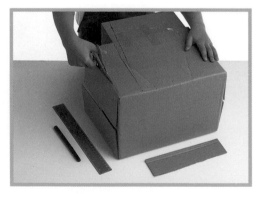

1 Cut off an end from one of the boxes. Slide the open end of the box inside the other box at right angles. Tape the two boxes together.

2 To make room for your head, cut a slit on each side of the end of the outside box, leaving a flap at the back. Trim boxes along line shown.

3 Draw and cut out two large ears on the leftover box pieces. Score a line down the middle of each ear with your scissors and fold the ears in half.

*Check with an adult first.
†Ask an adult for help when using a craft knife.

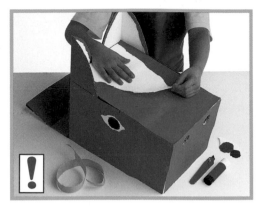

4 Cover the backs of the ears with brown paper and the insides with white and brown paper. Tape the ears to the top back corners of the head.

5 To cover the horse's head, cut out some brown paper to fit the front, top, back, and sides of the box. Glue it in place with the glue stick.

6 Cut two nostril holes at the front of the head to act as eyeholes.★ Glue on pieces of paper for a blaze, eyes, and a strip of yellow as a mouth.

7 To make the mane, fold one sheet of black crêpe paper to a width of 18 cm. Cut narrow strips into the folds, stopping 2 cm from the top.

8 Open out the mane and glue it to the centre back of the head and neck, making sure you leave a piece of mane for the horse's fringe.

9 Fold up the black crêpe paper fringe to fit the space between the horse's ears. Then carefully glue the fringe in place.

Making the body

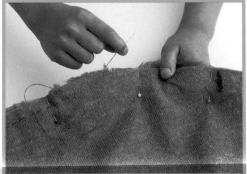

1 Fold the fabric in half lengthwise, fur side in, to make a rectangle (120 cm x 80 cm). Place the fold to your right.

2 Cut a curve in the top left hand corner. Start pinning the fabric 30 cm from the fold at the top and finish 36 cm from the bottom edge.

3 Sew along the edges you have pinned, leaving a 5 cm hole for the horse's tail marked on the curve★. Turn the fabric fur side out.

★Turn to page 235 for sewing tips.

HORSING AROUND

Making the tail

Making the hooves

1 Use a folded sheet of black crêpe paper. Cut narrow strips along it, as you did for the mane, stopping 4 cm from the top of the paper.

2 Bunch the tail together and wind sticky tape around the top. Then push it into the hole in the body and secure it in place with tape.

Draw and cut four shapes out of thin black card, as shown. Bend the hooves until they fit neatly around your feet and fasten the edges with tape.

Ready to gallop!

It takes a bit of practice for two people to move about in a horse costume. Don't forget that the person at the back can't see where you are going, so walk together slowly before trying to gallop.

Changing places
The person at the back of the horse can get hot inside the furry body and it's hard work bending down, so do swap places.

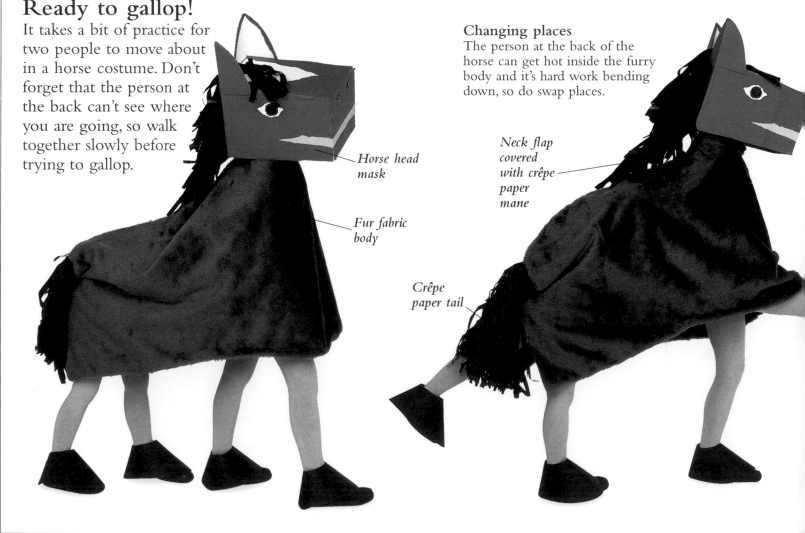

Horse head mask

Fur fabric body

Neck flap covered with crêpe paper mane

Crêpe paper tail

Putting on the costume

1 Put on your hooves. Your friend puts his or her head through the neck hole. Now help your friend put the mask on.

2 Pull the body straight and lift it up at the back ready to put the costume on. Remember to make sure that the tail is untangled.

3 Bend over and pull the back of the horse costume down over you. Put your arms around your friend's waist and get ready to walk!

Zippy zebra
Make a zebra costume in the same way as the pantomime horse. Just use black and white fur fabric for the body and draw large black lines on white paper for the mask.

White, brown, and black paper eyes

It is a good idea for both people to wear matching leggings or trousers.

Pantomime act
As part of a show, a pantomime horse can really make the audience laugh. Try dancing to music and hopping from one foot to another. End your show by curtsying with both pairs of legs. Try not to fall over!

Bend the card hooves around your feet and fasten the edges together at the back with sticky tape.

SPACE-AGE ROBOT

To create your own robot costume look for interesting pieces of packaging around your home. The main item is the helmet. You will need a carton big enough to cover most of your head. We used a popcorn carton painted blue but if you can't find a carton try a small box instead. Decorate it with bright colours to create a friendly robot or try using black and silver to create a scary robot.

EQUIPMENT

Pen

Scissors

Craft knife ★

Foam balls

Silver stars

Coloured braid

Circular lid

You will need

T-shirt

A round carton

Pipe cleaners

PVA glue

Coloured card

Bottle tops

Making the helmet

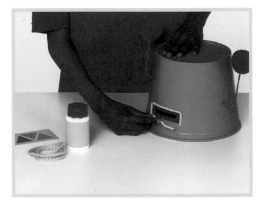

1 Try the carton on your head and mark an eyehole. Cut a long rectangular slot around the marks so you can see out of the helmet.

2 Stick a foam ball on the end of two pipe cleaners. Make two tiny holes in the sides of the carton and push the pipe cleaners into them.

3 Bend the pipe cleaners upwards. Glue card and pipe cleaners around the eye slot and decorate the carton with shapes of coloured card.

Decorating the T-shirt

1 Paint the circular lid bright colours and glue a bottle top in the middle of it. Glue short pieces of braid inside the lid, as shown.

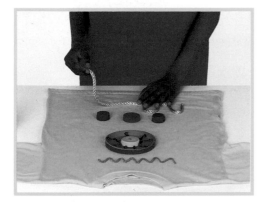

2 Glue the lid in the centre of the T-shirt to look like a control panel. Stick on bottle tops and wiggly lines of braid to decorate the T-shirt.

Robot power

The helmet and T-shirt give you the basis for your robot costume. Turn to page 158 for ideas of more things to add to your outfit. Don't forget to move your arms and legs in a stiff, jerky way like a robot!

Robot head

The finished helmet provides a complete disguise as it will cover your face and no-one will be able to see your eyes. The wobbly antennae will pick up any robot radar messages!

Foam ball antenna

Panel of coloured card decorated with card triangles

Tape the pipe cleaner securely inside the helmet.

Eye slot edged with coloured card and pipe cleaners

Circular lid decorated with a bottle top and coloured braid

Plastic bottle tops for switches

Wiggly lines of coloured braid

T-shirt
You can decorate the T-shirt with anything you can find. Just match the colours to the helmet you have made.

147

SPOOKS AND HORRORS

Perhaps it's Hallowe'en. It's dark outside, ghouls and spooks are about, and you want to join in the ghostly fun. Or maybe you just want to give your friends a terrifying fright. Here you can find out how to use an old sheet or pillowcase* to transform yourself into a ghoulish ghost and a horror mummy that look as if they've just stepped out of a horror movie.

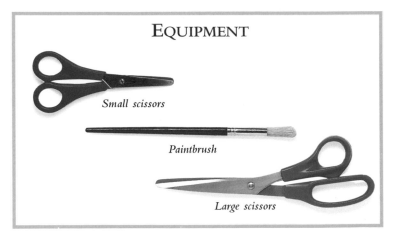

EQUIPMENT

Small scissors

Paintbrush

Large scissors

You will need

Large white sheet, tablecloth, or piece of fabric

Black felt

PVA glue   *Coloured tape*

Ghoulish ghost

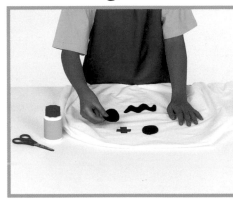

1 Put the sheet on and mark your eye positions with tape. Take off the sheet and cut out felt eyes and a mouth. Glue these over the tape.

2 Glue the felt mouth below the two eyes. Pinch each felt eye and cut a small hole in the middle of it, through both the felt and sheet.

Ghoulish ghost
Practise flitting silently around the house in your ghost costume. Slowly raise your arms and let out a spine-chilling moan.

Black felt eyes

Black felt mouth

Trim the bottom of the sheet so that it is straight.

3 Put the sheet on again, with the eye holes in the right place. Ask an adult to trim around the bottom of the sheet, to make a straight hem.

Horror mummy

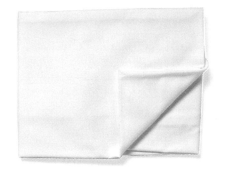

White pillowcase

Torn strips of a white sheet or cotton fabric

Coloured tape

Red paint

1 Put the pillowcase on and mark the position of your face. Take the pillowcase off, cut a hole for the face and trim the bottom off the pillowcase.

2 Put the pillowcase back on. Ask a friend to loosely wind strips of fabric around your head, to hold the pillowcase in place.

Finishing touches

Ask your friend to paint a red ear "wound" on the side of your head. Then bend one arm across your stomach so it can be bandaged up. You can also bandage your free arm and hand.

Blood-splattered "wound"

Bind the arm and hand with another strip of fabric.

Wind the bandage loosely around your head.

Arm hidden by the bandage sling

Wear old clothes and fringe the edges using scissors.★

Dab more red paint around any holes in your clothes, for an extra-gory effect.

KNIGHT IN ARMOUR

Here and overleaf you can see how to make a suit of shining armour, a sword, and a dagger worthy of the most valiant knight. Everything is made of corrugated card from cardboard boxes and extra-wide aluminium foil. Before you make the breastplate, measure yourself and adapt the armour pattern to fit your body.

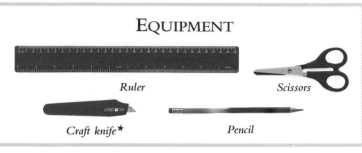

EQUIPMENT

Ruler

Scissors

Craft knife★

Pencil

You will need

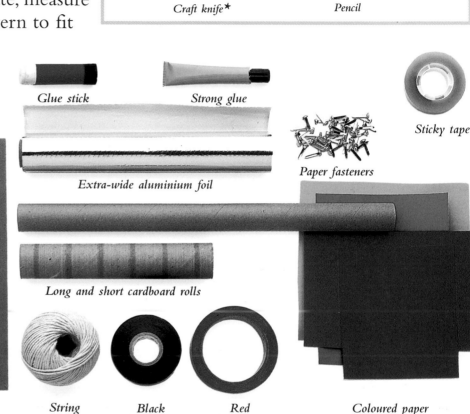

Glue stick

Strong glue

Sticky tape

Extra-wide aluminium foil

Paper fasteners

Long and short cardboard rolls

Thick corrugated card

String

Black coloured tape

Red coloured tape

Coloured paper

Making the breastplate

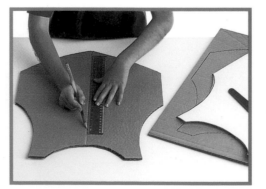

1 Draw a breastplate pattern on paper, with the neck and arm-holes 20 cm wide. The distance from the neck to the waist should be 37 cm.

2 Using this pattern, draw and cut two breastplates out of corrugated card. Score a line and make a fold down the middle of each breastplate.

3 Cut out two strips of card 3.5 cm x 40 cm. Cover these straps and the breastplates with foil, taping it in place at the back of each piece.

Ask an adult for help when using a craft knife.

4 Make two holes at the top of each breastplate. Attach the straps to the breastplates with paper fasteners, adjusting the lengths to fit.

5 Make three holes down the sides of each breastplate. Thread a long piece of string through the holes, as you would thread a shoelace.

6 Decorate the front breastplate with paper fasteners, as shown. Make a paper shield design and glue it to the middle of the breastplate.

Making the shield

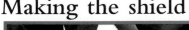

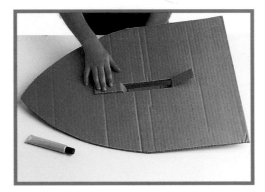

1 Cut two shields out of corrugated card 50 cm x 40 cm, as shown. Cut out a slot 12.5 cm long and 2.5 cm wide in the middle of one shield.

2 Cut out a strip of strong card 2.25 cm wide and 23 cm long. Fold it to make a handle. Push it in the slot and glue the ends in place.

3 Glue the shields together, with the handle at the back. Seal the edges with sticky tape. Decorate the shield with a coloured paper design.

Making the helmet

1 Cut out a rectangle of card 80 cm x 30 cm. Tape it into a pointed cylinder shape. Make a top for the helmet and tape it in place.

2 Try the helmet on. Then draw and cut out curves along the bottom edge of the helmet so that it sits comfortably on your shoulders.

3 Cut four slits in the front of the helmet, for eye holes. Cover the helmet with foil and decorate with paper fasteners and a paper shield.

ON GUARD!

Weapon blades

Flatten two cardboard tubes, one long and one short. Cut one end of each tube into a point. Tape the ends. Cover the tubes with foil, taping the join.

Dagger handle

Cut out a rectangle of card 17 cm x 6 cm and make a slit in the centre. Slide the short blade through the slit, fold the card in half, and tape down.

Sword handle

Cut★ a piece of card 34 cm x 8 cm with rounded ends. Cover with black tape and cut two slits each end, wide enough to push the sword through.

Finishing touches

Bend the sword handle as shown. Slide it over the top of the sword. Wrap tape around the blade to keep the handle in place. Decorate with coloured tape.

Gauntlets

Cut two boat-shaped pieces of card to fit around your wrists. Cover each one with foil and tape the ends together. Decorate with fasteners.

Shield
Decorate the shield with coloured paper to look like a coat of arms. You can copy this one or make up a design of your own.

Yellow paper stripe

Green paper diamonds

Red paper

Decorate the helmet with a mini shield bearing your coat of arms.

Helmet
The helmet should fit comfortably over your head and sit on your shoulders.

Slits for eye holes

Dagger
The dagger can be worn slung from your belt. See page 158 for more ideas.

Straight handle decorated with black and red coloured tape

The dagger has a short blade

Ready for action
When dressing up as a knight put on your breastplate, then your gauntlets, and finally your helmet. You can make arm and shoulder plates and leg guards in the same way as the gauntlets.

Shoulder plate fixed to breastplate with sticky tape

Breastplate
The breastplate will slip over your head more easily if you loosen the string ties on either side.

Sword
The sword has a long blade and a curved black guard.

Paper fasteners look like studs

String tie for fastening the sides of the breastplate

Gauntlet
These are decorated with paper fasteners.

Smaller version of the shield's coat of arms

Dark gloves complete the gauntlet

FIENDISH DEVIL

On the days when you feel like being really devilish, this is the costume for you. Like many successful costumes it relies on a simply decorated T-shirt and a few cunning accessories for its effect; in this case curved horns and a pointed tail. You will need a really big T-shirt to decorate – it should be long enough to reach your thighs.

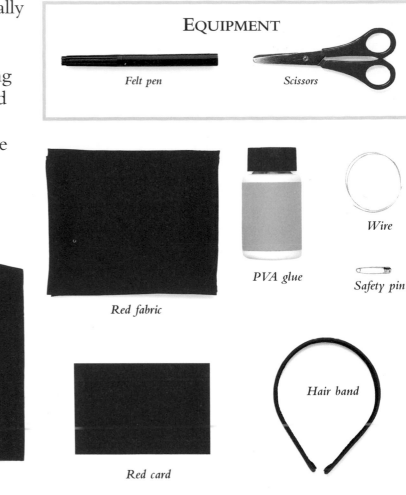

EQUIPMENT

Felt pen

Scissors

Red fabric

PVA glue

Wire

Safety pin

You will need

Orange and yellow felt

Red T-shirt

Red card

Hair band

Decorating the T-shirt

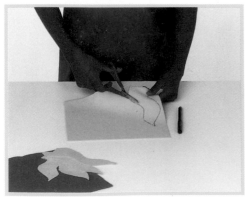

1 Draw flame shapes on pieces of felt and cut them out. Make the orange flames smaller and narrower than the yellow ones.

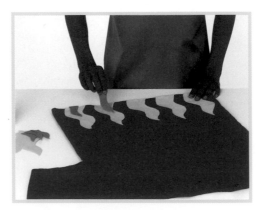

2 Glue yellow flames along the bottom of the T-shirt, then glue the orange ones on top. Do the same with the sleeves and shoulders.

Horns

Draw two small, curved horns on the red card and cut them out. Carefully glue them to the front of the hair band, as shown.

Pointed tail

1 Cut out a strip of fabric 100 cm x 10 cm. Fold the fabric in half (100 cm x 5 cm), right side in. Glue the long edges together like a tube.

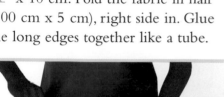

2 When the ... safety pin ... Thread the ... turn the f...

3 Thread 65 cm of wire inside the tail. Cut out two triangles and glue them together over one end of the tube and glue the other end shut.

Feeling devilish

To complete the costume, attach the tail to the back of the T-shirt with a large safety pin and pull on a pair of red tights.

Horns
The curved horns are made of red card stuck to the front of a hair band.

Make two extra-long flames to stick to the shoulders of the T-shirt.

T-shirt
A large, red T-shirt is decorated with yellow and orange felt flames.

Pointed tail
...unch the fabric up as you ... the wire into the tail, ...e it look pleated.

Two triangles of red card glued together

COSTUME PARADE

You have made masks, hats, cloaks, tunics, and full outfits. Here, and over the page, you can see how simple accessories can complete an array of dazzling costumes.

Hat (page 116)

Cloak (page 138)

Black gloves

Wand

Long, black T-shirt

Ghost costume (page 148)

Chain

Black tights

Black tights

Ghoulish ghost

Starry witch

Paper fringes tied around wrists and ankles

Orange trousers and sweatshirt

Mask (page 124)

Mask (page 124)

Cape (page 140)

Feathered cape (page 140)

Mask (page 124)

Socks on hands

Pink T-shirt

Webbed feet cut out of yellow card and taped around ankles

Yellow tights

Green tights

Wild lion

Evil insect

Exotic bird

156

Robot costume (page 146)

Shoulder guards made from coloured card

Gauntlets (see armour, page 152)

Leg guards made in same way as gauntlets

Feet (see horse's hooves, page 144)

Space-age robot

Moustache (page 120)

Hat (page 116)

Star-shaped badge (page 112)

Smart sheriff

Jewels (page 113)

Movie-star shades (page 119)

Gold shirt

Glamorous movie star

Hat (page 14)

Red foam ball nose

Ra-ra skirt (page 133) worn as neck ruff

Cheerful clown

Glasses (page 119) with pop-out eyes

Hair spiked with gel

Yellow overalls

Mad professor

Starry hair band

Starry wand (page 113)

Transparent cape (page 140)

Skirt (page 132)

Good fairy

Devil costume (page 154)

Cape (page 140)

Trident

Red tights

Fiendish devil

Bandaged head (page 149)

Tattered clothes

Bandaged arm and hand

Bandaged feet

Horror mummy

157

COSTUME PARADE

Costume
(page 142)

Mask and body
(page 145)

Black card
hooves

Pantomime horse

Zippy zebra

Hat and bendy
plaits (page 121)

T-shirt

Dungarees

Basket of
carrots

Farm girl

Hat
(page 116)

Paper
garland
flowers

Sword
(page 152)

Grass skirt
(page 132)

Hula-hula girl

Eye patch
(page 118)

Swashbuckling pirate

Paper flower
in hair

Sarong
and top
(page 136)

Desert island dancer

Jewels
(page 112)

Toga
(page 137)

Roman emperor

Felt hat

Shades
(page 119)

Moustache
(page 120)

Wool
eyebrows
stuck to tape

Beard
(page 120)

Yellow
raincoat

Undercover detective

Jolly fisherman

Turban
(page 137)

Chocolate
coins

Rich sultan

Chef's hat

Moustache
(page 120)

Master chef

Bow and arrow

Tunic
(page 135)

Dagger
(page 152)

Forest archer

Tall hat
(page 116)

Jewelled mask

Royal robe
(page 139)

Medieval damsel

Top hat
(page 116)

Cloak
(page 138)

Magic
scarf

Amazing magician

Crown (page 116)

Shields and weapons
(page 151 and 152)

Body armour
(page 150)

Long T-shirt

Tunic
(page 134)

Leg guards
made the
same way as
gauntlets

Knights in armour

Royal robe
(page 139)

Purple sash

Sword
(page 152)

Gold
cardboard
buckles

Noble king

159

SPILLIKINS

This is a game for steady hands that comes from China. In the past, players used delicate ivory or thin wooden sticks painted with bands of colour. The sticks were also used for fortune telling. You can use skewers instead of sticks in this game for two or more players.

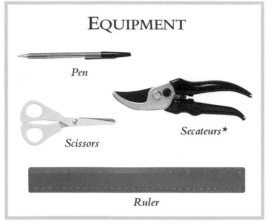

EQUIPMENT

Pen

Scissors

Secateurs★

Ruler

You will need

Red and blue tape

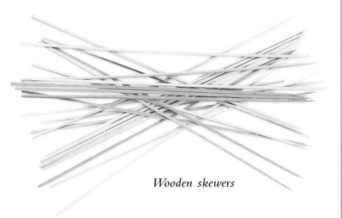

Wooden skewers

Yellow ribbon

Ribbon tied tightly in a bow

Finished Spillikins

When you have finished playing the game, tie a ribbon around the spillikins to store them neatly.

Making the sticks

1 Measure and mark 30 skewers, making them all the same length. Ask an adult to trim the points off the skewers by using the secateurs.

2 Cut some short lengths of red and blue tape. Wind these around the sticks, using the list opposite as a guide to where to place the tape.

Make up the following sticks:

6 skewers with one red band

6 skewers with two red bands

2 skewers with three red bands

2 skewers with two red and blue bands

6 skewers with one blue band

6 skewers with two blue bands

2 skewers with three blue bands

How to play

The aim of the game is to remove as many sticks from the central pile as you can, without moving any other stick.

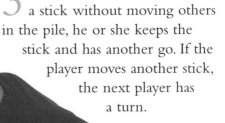

1 Players sit in a circle. One player holds the spillikins and rests the ends on a table or the floor.

2 Let the spillikins drop so that they fall in a jumbled heap. Each player takes a turn in carefully removing a stick from the central pile.

Trim the ribbon so that it doesn't fray.

3 If a player manages to remove a stick without moving others in the pile, he or she keeps the stick and has another go. If the player moves another stick, the next player has a turn.

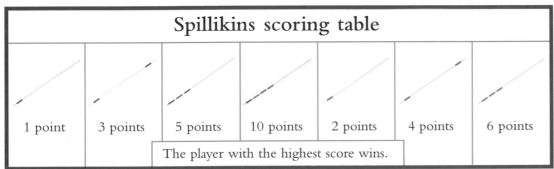

4 When all the sticks have been taken, players check their scores using the table below to find the winner.

Player's pile of sticks

Spillikins scoring table

1 point	3 points	5 points	10 points	2 points	4 points	6 points
			The player with the highest score wins.			

Game origins

Spillikins was traditionally played by the emperors of Ancient China. During the Ming Dynasty, an emperor built a palace in Beijing called the Forbidden City.

MANCALA

Mancala is a board game from Africa for two people, played by children and adults. It has many different names and rules. The board is sometimes made from wood, but is often just a series of holes scooped out of the ground. Placing the game pieces on the board is called "sowing". Beans, shells, or stones are traditionally used as game pieces, but you can use beads instead.

You will need

1 kg air-hardening modelling clay

Plain flour

Poster paints

48 beads

Tubes of all-purpose fabric paint★

EQUIPMENT

Thin paintbrush

Thick paintbrush

Knife

Saucer

Pepper pot

Rolling pin

Mug

Glass of water

Ruler

Making the board

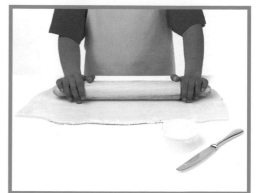

1 Spread some plain flour on to a clean surface. Roll out the air-hardening modelling clay evenly with the rolling pin.

2 Cut a 50 cm x 10 cm board out of the clay. With the pepper pot, make 12 indents. Using the mug, put two indents at each end for stores.

3 Leave the clay board to harden and dry. Paint and decorate the board and paint one row of indents yellow and the other row red.

★*Available from large department stores or craft shops.*

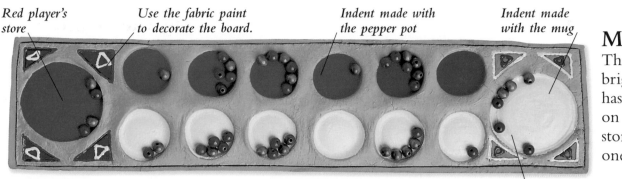

Red player's store

Use the fabric paint to decorate the board.

Indent made with the pepper pot

Indent made with the mug

Mancala board
The finished board is brightly coloured and has 6 indents or holes on each side with a store on each end, one for each player.

Yellow player's store

How to play
Each player starts with 24 beads. The object of the game is to capture the most beads.

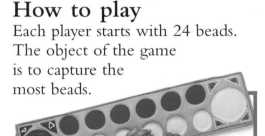

Sow one bead into each hole in an anti-clockwise direction.

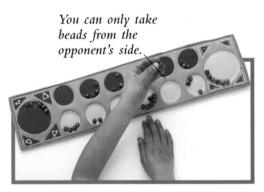

You can only take beads from the opponent's side.

1 Players sit either side of the board and put 4 beads in each hole on their row. Each player has an extra hole on their right to act as a store.

2 Each player scoops the beads out of any hole on his or her side and sows the beads one at a time into each hole anti-clockwise round the board.

3 If the last bead is dropped into an opponent's hole and the beads total 2 or 3, then the player scoops the beads up and puts them in the store.

4 If the hole immediately preceeding the now empty hole also has 2 or 3 beads, then the player may also take these beads. The game ends when a player has no beads left on his or her row. The winner is the player with the most beads in his or her store.

Game origins
Mancala is a popular game played by Africans from all over the continent. Africa contains 50 different countries and has varied landscapes including deserts, mountains, rainforests, and grass plains.

HYENA CHASE

This game for three or more players comes from Sudan, a country in Central Africa that is mainly desert. Each circle on the game board represents one day's travel by the village women to reach a well in the desert to wash their clothes. The journey can be long, and in this game there is the added danger of being eaten by a hyena!

Coloured felt

You will need

Coloured ribbon

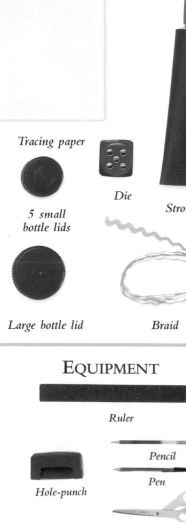

Tracing paper

5 small bottle lids

Die

Strong glue

Large bottle lid

Braid

Making the game

1 Measure and cut out some brown felt 50 cm x 50 cm. Cut four strips of green felt 50 cm long and glue to each edge. Decorate with braid.

2 Using a large bottle lid, draw 42 circles on a piece of beige felt. Then cut the circles out. Cut out small triangles for the arrows.

EQUIPMENT

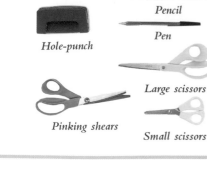

Ruler

Pencil

Hole-punch

Pen

Large scissors

Pinking shears

Small scissors

3 Glue the circles to the board in a spiral with the arrows in between. Cut out a hut, palm tree, and water jar and glue them in place on the board.

4 Draw a hyena and four women's heads on tracing paper. Transfer these on to felt and cut out. Glue each head to a small lid for counters.

How to play

Players take turns to throw the die and to travel to the well. They must return to the village before being eaten by the hyena!

Each circle represents a day's travel.

The village is the starting point.

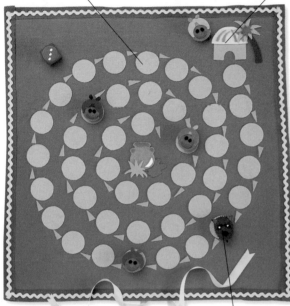

Roll the game up when finished and secure with ribbon.

Hyena counter

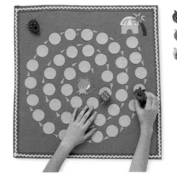

1 Players sit around the board and each chooses a village-woman counter. Players must throw a 6 to begin their journey to the well.

2 Players take it in turns to throw the die and move their counters the number of circles indicated. A 6 gives a second go.

3 When players reach the well, they stop and wash their clothes. They cannot start the return journey until a 6 is thrown.

4 The first player back to the village is the winner, but the game is not over: this player swaps the counter for the hyena.

5 The hyena travels to the well by moving twice the number shown on the die. When the hyena reaches the well, it drinks and returns to the village, eating up any counters it jumps over on the way.

Well

Game origins

Sudan is the largest country in Africa. The nomadic peoples of this region travel with their camels and goats in search of food and water.

Hyena chasing the village women

TRICKET

Tricket is a Colombian game of strategy for two players. Very similar to the game of Nine Men's Morris, which originated in Iceland, Tricket has travelled across the world from South America.

You will need

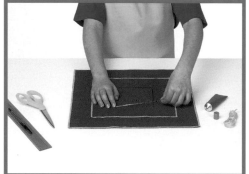

9 green gemstones★

9 blue gemstones★   *Coloured ribbon*

Coloured felt

Large button

EQUIPMENT

Pen

Scissors

Ruler

Strong glue

Making the board

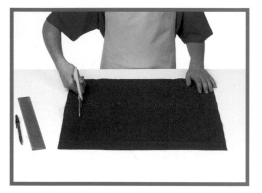

1 Using a ruler, measure and draw with a pen a 36 cm x 36 cm square on a large piece of felt. Cut out the square to make the board.

2 Inside the board, measure and draw two smaller squares. Glue thin ribbon around the board's edges and over the marked squares.

3 Glue more ribbon to connect the corners of each square. Then glue ribbon to connect the middles of each square's four sides, as shown.

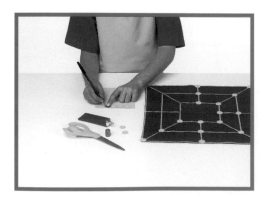

4 Trace around the button 24 times on a piece of felt. Cut out the felt circles and glue them to all the intersecting points on the board.

Tricket board

The tricket board is now ready to be used. The aim of the game is to form lines of three counters on the board.

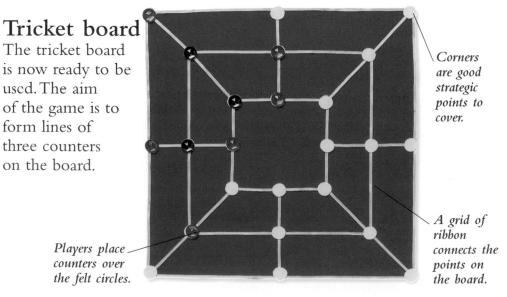

Corners are good strategic points to cover.

A grid of ribbon connects the points on the board.

Players place counters over the felt circles.

Playing the game

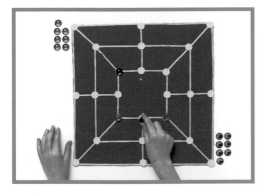

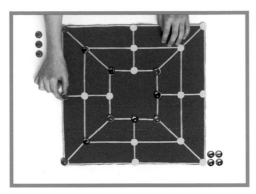

1 Each player has nine counters. The two players take it in turns to place their counters, one at a time, on any empty point on the board.

2 The object of the game is to form a line of three counters, all the same colour, called a tricket. Try to block your opponent's trickets as well.

3 When a player makes a line of three, he or she calls out "tricket" and then removes any one of the other player's counters from the board.

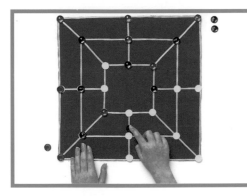

4 Once all of the counters have been placed on the board, the players move by sliding their counters to empty points on the board. A counter can only be moved to a point that adjoins the one it is on.

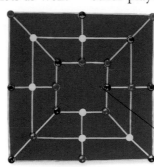

Blocking tactic
One way to win the game is to block your opponent's counters. This will leave your opponent without a point to move to.

The blue counters have blocked in the green counters.

Game origins
Spanish Conquistadores arrived in Colombia in the 16th century, bringing many new things from Europe, including their language and the game Tricket. The Conquistadores came to Colombia in search of local riches of gold and emeralds.

5 There are two ways to win tricket: you are the winner if the other player has only two counters left on the board, and you can also win by blocking in your opponent.

A tricket can be formed horizontally, vertically, or diagonally.

COWS AND LEOPARDS

Cows and Leopards is a traditional board game from Sri Lanka. The game was played outside and the board scratched into the ground using a stick. We have used coloured card for the board in this game for two players.

You will need

Coloured card

White card

Poster paints

PVA glue   Glue stick   26 Buttons

EQUIPMENT

Pencil

Scissors

Paintbrush

Saucer

Glass of water

Craft knife*

Ruler

Making the board

1 Cut out a piece of white card 40 cm x 40 cm. Draw a square 20 cm x 20 cm in the centre, and a triangle on each side, as shown.

2 Cut out of green card 32 triangles 4 x 4 x 5.5cm. Cut out eight triangles, 8 x 5 x 9 cm. Trim these in half widthwise to form two shapes.

3 Glue the 32 triangles on to the board within the drawn square. Leave a gap between each triangle. Fill the large triangles with the shapes.

4 Decorate the edges of the board with card to make it look like a jungle. Make sure that the card decorations fit around the game board.

Making the counters

5 Glue the pieces of card jungle to the board. Finally, cut four strips of blue card 40 cm long, and glue them to the edge of the game board.

Paint two buttons yellow and leave to dry. Put on brown and orange spots for leopards. Paint 24 buttons white and let dry. Dab on brown spots for cattle.

*Ask an adult for help when using a craft knife.

How to play

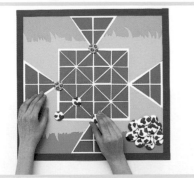

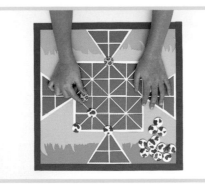

1 One player has 24 cow counters and one has two leopards. To start, players take turns to put the pieces, one at a time, on any points of the board.

2 Once both leopards have been positioned, they may move along the lines in any direction including diagonally, one point at each turn.

3 The leopard can kill a cow by leaping over it on to a vacant point immediately beyond the cow. The cow is removed from the board.

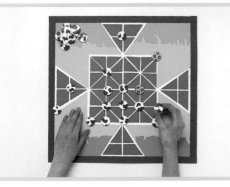

4 Before they can move, all 24 cow counters must be placed. The aim for the cows is to pen the leopards into a corner of the board so that they cannot move. The cows cannot jump over the leopards.

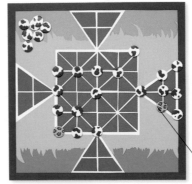

Penning in leopards
To prevent a leopard from moving, block all the points around the leopard with cow counters.

Penned in leopard

5 The player with the cow counters wins if he or she manages to pen in both leopards first. The leopards player wins if he or she removes all the cows.

Game origins
Sri Lanka is an island south of India with many national parks. The spotted leopard is a protected animal and hunts mainly at night.

Leopard leaping over the cow

BEETLE GAME

There are many variations of the Beetle Game and it has been played for many years. It is a great party game to play for between two and six players. Make a beetle board for each player to use.

You will need

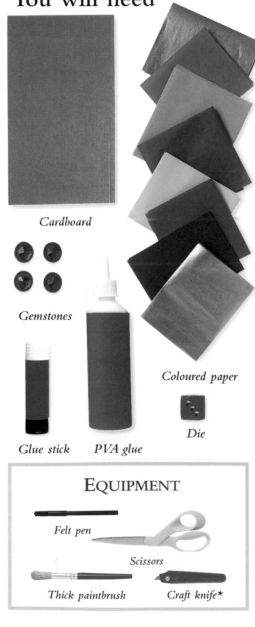

Cardboard

Gemstones

Glue stick   PVA glue

Coloured paper

Die

EQUIPMENT

Felt pen

Scissors

Thick paintbrush   Craft knife*

Making a beetle board

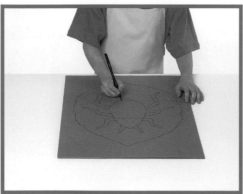

1 Draw a large leaf on a piece of cardboard. Inside the leaf, draw a beetle with a body, a head, six legs, two antennae, and a tail, as shown.

2 Ask an adult to cut the leaf out with the craft knife and then carefully cut out the body of the beetle, the legs, and the antennae.

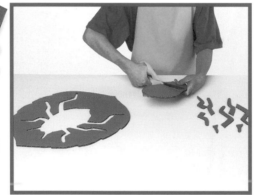

3 Push the legs and antennae out of the leaf. Using the scissors, carefully cut the head and the tail from the body, as shown.

4 To make eyes, trace around the gemstones on the beetle head. Ask an adult to cut out the eyeholes with the craft knife.

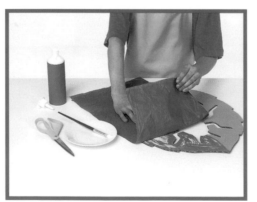

5 Brush glue on to the leaf and then cover each half with a sheet of coloured paper. Once the glue is dry, trim around the leaf.

6 Cover the beetle in gold or silver paper. Trim any excess paper off the beetle. Decorate the beetle with twisted strips of paper.

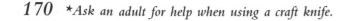

Finished Beetle Game

The finished beetle pieces fit snugly into the leaf board. Each player selects a separate board. Start the game by pressing out the beetle parts.

Use different coloured paper for each player's board.

How to play

1 Each player must throw a 6 on the die to start. Once a player has thrown a 6, he or she can place the body in the leaf.

2 When the body is in place, the player throws the die and puts in the beetle body part represented by the number on the die.

3 After each throw, the next player has a turn. The first player to complete his or her beetle wins.

The eyes and antennae can only be placed on the beetle after the head is positioned.

Place the legs, eyes, and antennae one at a time.

If a player has the part represented on the die already on the board, the turn passes to the next player.

The remaining pieces of beetle go on the leaf.

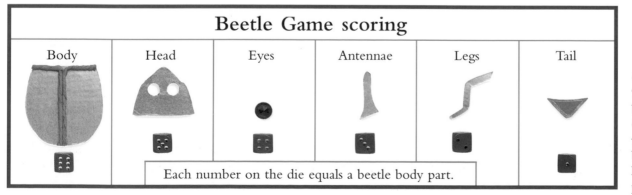

Beetle Game scoring

Body	Head	Eyes	Antennae	Legs	Tail

Each number on the die equals a beetle body part.

Game origins

The Beetle Game has been a popular game in Great Britain for many years. Traditionally, the beetle is styled on the ladybird and the beetle parts are drawn on paper.

BASKET GAME

This dice game of chance is called the Basket Game or Monshimunh and it was invented by the Cheyenne Indians. These Native Americans played this game and often used smoothed bone or peach stones as the dice in the basket. You can use pebbles or stones instead. The dice were marked with symbols of bears' paws and faces. This is a game for four or more players.

You will need

Small round basket

Clear varnish

Poster paint

*32 straws
(8 tally sticks
per player)*

5 flat stones

Making the dice

EQUIPMENT

Glass of water

Saucer

Pencil

Paintbrush

1 Wash all five stones. Choose three flat stones. Mark a bear's paw on one side of each stone. Then paint the bear's paw in yellow on each stone.

2 Draw and then paint a cross in green on one side of the other two stones. When the paint is dry, varnish the stones and leave to dry.

How to play

The aim of the game is to be the first player to collect eight tally sticks.

1 Sit in a circle. Place all the tally sticks in a central pile. Put the stone dice into the basket. Each player gently tosses the stones up and catches them in the basket.

Toss up the dice and catch them in the basket.

Blank side of dice

Bear's paw

The cross on the dice represents a face.

2 After each throw, look at the dice and see which way they have landed. To score, check the winning combinations at the bottom of the page.

3 If you have scored, take the correct number of tally sticks and play again. If you have not scored, pass the basket to the next person in the circle.

Central pile of tally sticks

Player's tally sticks

Basket Game scoring

take	take	take	take	take

No score for all other dice combinations

Game origins

The Basket Game was played by the Cheyenne Indians who lived in the Oklahoma plains and the Rocky Mountains of North America. The Rockies stretch from Alaska to Mexico and are home to grizzly bears.

FIVE-STONE JACKS

Games with Jacks are played in countries all over the world. Traditionally, players used the knucklebones of sheep for playing pieces. In India, children play a version of Jacks called Pacheta. Since India is a hot country, Pacheta is played outside on dry ground using small stones. This is a game for two or more players.

You will need

Poster paints

Clear varnish

EQUIPMENT

Paintbrush

Saucer　　*Pencil*　　*Glass of water*

5 small flat stones

Making the jacks

1 Choose five small stones and clean them. Carefully mark a shape on each stone and then paint them in different colours as shown.

2 Carefully varnish each stone to protect the paint on the stones. Leave the stones to dry fully before using them in the game.

SHELL GAME

This is a game using shells called Izingendo, which Zulu children in South Africa play. It is an ideal game for the beach for two players.

1 Dig a hole in the sand. Put five shells in the hole and throw a shell in the air. Using the same hand, try to scoop all the shells out of the hole, and catch the thrown shell.

Scoop the shells out of the hole.

You will need

20 small shells

How to play

1 Take all five stones in the palm of your hand. Keeping your hand in front of you, throw the stones up about 15 cm in the air.

2 As the stones are coming down, try to catch them on the back of your hand. Keep your fingers together so that the stones don't slip through.

3 Throw the stones from the back of your hand into your palm. The player who has caught the most stones starts the game.

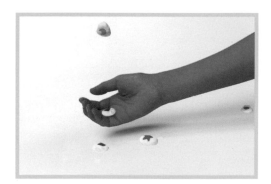

4 Scatter the stones on the ground. Throw one stone in the air, pick up a stone from the ground and catch the thrown stone with the same hand.

5 Repeat until you have picked up all the stones. Scatter the stones again, throw one in the air and pick up the remaining stones in pairs.

6 Then pick up three stones, and four stones. If you miss, the other player has a go. You start from where you finished when you have a new turn.

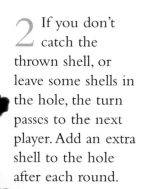

2 If you don't catch the thrown shell, or leave some shells in the hole, the turn passes to the next player. Add an extra shell to the hole after each round.

7 Make an arch with your forefinger and thumb. Scatter the stones, throw one up and tap one stone through the arch. Repeat for each stone. Then do pairs, threes, and fours.

To finish the game, throw up a stone and scoop up the other stones.

PAPER, SCISSORS, STONE

This fast-moving hand game from Japan was originally called Jan Ken Pon, meaning paper, sword, fist. Each of two players must beat the other player in a quick show of hands.

Hand positions

 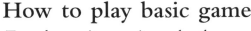 

A clenched fist represents a stone.

Two fingers represent scissors.

A flat hand represents paper.

Scoring

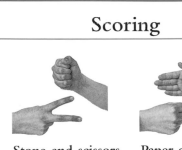

Stone and scissors Stone wins, as stone blunts scissors.

Paper and stone Paper wins, as paper wraps stone.

Symbols the same Two of the same symbols is a draw.

Scissors and paper Scissors win, as scissors cut paper.

How to play basic game

Two players sit opposite each other. Both players clench a fist and chant "Jan Ken Pon". On the word Pon, both players display a hand in one of the three positions shown above.

A clenched fist represents a stone.

In this case, paper wraps stone and wins this round.

THE WARRIOR GAME

This game comes from New Zealand and is called Hei Tama Tu Tama. It is a game for two players who must move quickly in order to win the game.

How to play

1 Two players stand with their hands on their hips. One is the defender and calls out "One, Hei Tama Tu Tama". On the last word, both players display one of the four arm positions shown below.

Arm positions

Hand positions

Finger pointing to the left

Finger pointing straight down

Finger pointing to the right

Finger pointing straight up

Game origins

Intricate designs made with paper and scissors are part of Japan's ancient culture and the art of origami paper folding originated here. Japanese children still dress up in the traditional costume called the Kimono for special occasions.

How to play extended game

The winning player chants "Atchi Muiti Hoi" and points a finger in one direction. At the same time, the other player moves his or her head, trying to avoid the same direction as the winner.

If the hand and the head positions mirror each other the player pointing wins.

If the hand and head positions are different the round is a draw.

Head positions

Head up

Head to the left

Head to the right

Head down

2 If both players choose the same position, the defender wins a point and continues calling. If they choose different positions, neither player scores and the challenger calls the next round.

A point can only be scored by the defender calling the round.

Scoring

After winning a point, the player starts the next round by calling out "Two, Hei Tama Tu Tama". The first player to reach Ten, Hei Tama Tu Tama wins the game. The scoring moves on only when a point is won.

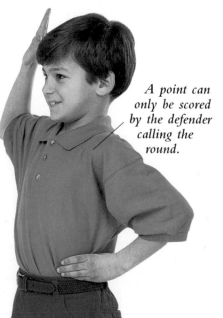

Game origins

The Maoris from New Zealand thought that hand and arm games were good practice for warriors, helping them develop quick reactions.

MARBLE GAMES

Glass marbles were very popular in Victorian England. Players competed in games to win marbles from each other. Here is a collection of traditional marble games for two or more players.

You will need

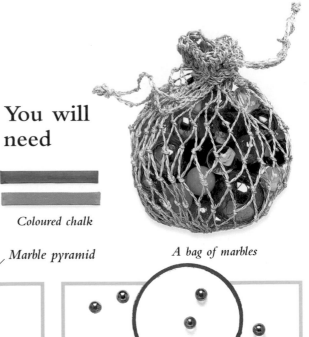

Coloured chalk

A bag of marbles

Marble Pyramid

Marble games are sometimes played on the pavement sprinkled with dirt or damp sand. Players can use chalk to draw a circle directly on to the ground or smooth paved area.

Marble pyramid

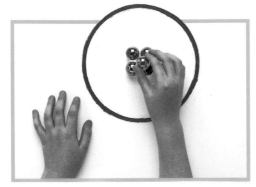

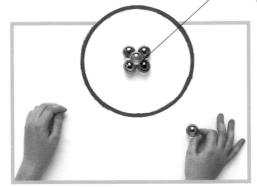

1 Draw a big circle with chalk. One player is keeper and makes a five-marble pyramid in the circle, charging the other players one marble per turn.

2 The other players take turns to shoot a marble at the pyramid from 1 metre away. Each player keeps any marbles knocked out of the circle.

3 Marbles remaining inside the circle remain the property of the keeper. The keeper must rebuild the pyramid after each player's turn.

Bounce Eye

In Bounce Eye, players knock the marbles out of a circle by dropping a marble from eye height.

2 The first player drops a marble from head height on to the cluster, keeping any marbles driven out of the circle. If none of the marbles are knocked out, the first player adds another marble, reforms the cluster, and the next player has a turn.

1 Draw a chalk circle about 30 cm in diameter on the ground. Each player puts one marble in the centre of the circle to form a cluster.

The cluster of marbles scatters when a marble is dropped in to the circle.

Hundreds

For this game, players need to practise shooting marbles accurately in order to roll them inside a circle target.

How to shoot a marble

Flick the marble with your forefinger

Flick the marble with your thumb

How to play

Two players shoot a marble from behind a line that is drawn 3 metres from a chalk circle. If only one player's marble stops in the circle, this player scores 10 points. If both or neither of the marbles stop in the circle, both players shoot again.

The first player to score 100 points is the winner.

Picking Plums

This game for two players requires a steady aim. The marble used for shooting is often bigger than an ordinary marble and is called a taw or shooter. Retrieve the taw after each turn.

Game origins

Marble games have been played throughout the centuries and appeared as early as Ancient Roman times. Roman children played games with marbles made of clay or glass.

How to play

Each player places two marbles in a straight line on the ground, 3 cm apart, to form a line of plums. Players take turns to shoot from a second line 1.5 metres away, aiming to pick the plums, or to hit the marbles. Players keep any marbles they hit.

The line of plums or marbles

Shooting a taw

179

POLE GAMES

Here are two outdoor games from Brazil that use the same pole and then either hoops and stones to throw. With practice, your throws will become more accurate.

You will need

For Hit It Off

Coloured tapes

EQUIPMENT

Scissors

2 stones per player

For the Hoop Game

4 embroidery hoops 20 cm across

Coloured tape

Wooden pole 2 metres long

Twig or stick

Plastic counters or bottle tops

Hit It Off

This game for two players relies on an accurate eye and careful aim. Make sure that both players stand on the same side of the circle so that neither player gets hit by a stone.

Decorating the pole

To decorate the pole, stick long strips of yellow and white tape down its length. Cover the whole pole to protect it from knocks and scratches.

Push the pole into the ground.

Use a twig to mark the circles in the ground.

How to play

1 Hammer the pole into the ground. Balance a counter or bottle top on the top of the pole. Mark two circles round the pole, one 50 cm away and another 1 metre away.

The Hoop Game

This is a game for two or more players. Throw a hoop over a pole to score points.

Decorating the hoops

Use the inside rings of four embroidery hoops. Completely cover two hoops in blue tape, and two hoops in red, as shown.

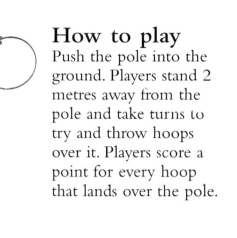

How to play

Push the pole into the ground. Players stand 2 metres away from the pole and take turns to try and throw hoops over it. Players score a point for every hoop that lands over the pole.

Use the same pole made for Hit It Off.

Aim the stone at the top of the pole and try to knock off the counter.

2 Players stand away from the outer circle and take turns throwing a stone to try and knock the counter off the pole. If the counter falls into the inner circle, the player scores one point. If the counter falls into the outer circle, the player scores two points.

Placing the counter

Each time a counter falls, replace it by carefully positioning another on the top of the pole.

Winning the game

The winner is the player with the highest total of points after an agreed number of throws.

181

LIMBO

An energetic game for any number of players, Limbo can be played inside, outside, in the garden, or on the beach. Turn on some lively music and take turns in passing as low as possible under the bar!

You will need

Coloured tapes

Modelling clay

Sticky tape

Dowelling

Card

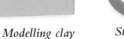

Bamboo poles

EQUIPMENT

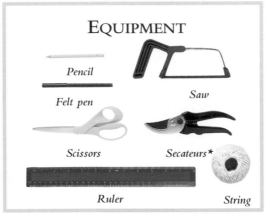

Pencil

Felt pen

Saw

Scissors

Secateurs★

Ruler

String

Making the limbo bar

1 Ask an adult to cut two bamboo poles, each 1 metre long. Cut ten 5 cm rods from the dowelling and tape these 20 cm apart on the poles.

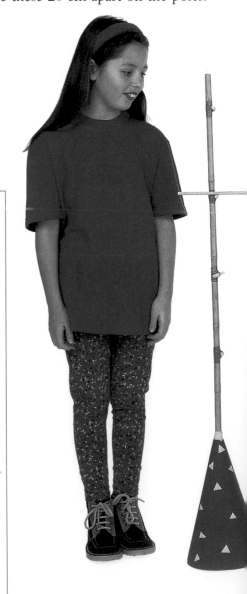

Go Limbo!

A different way to do the Limbo is to crawl under the bar. Make sure that as each player wriggles under the crossbar it isn't touched or knocked off the rods.

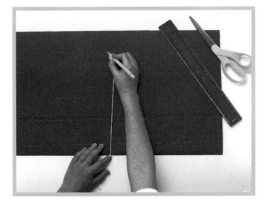

2 Cut out some card 50 cm x 25 cm. Using the pencil and the string, draw a semicircle on the card, as shown. Cut out the semicircle.

3 Carefully roll the cut-out card into a cone. Tape the join securely. Trim off the top of the cone, so that it will slip over the end of the pole.

4 Slip the cone over the bottom end of the pole and tape it in place. Place some modelling clay on the end of the pole to weigh it down.

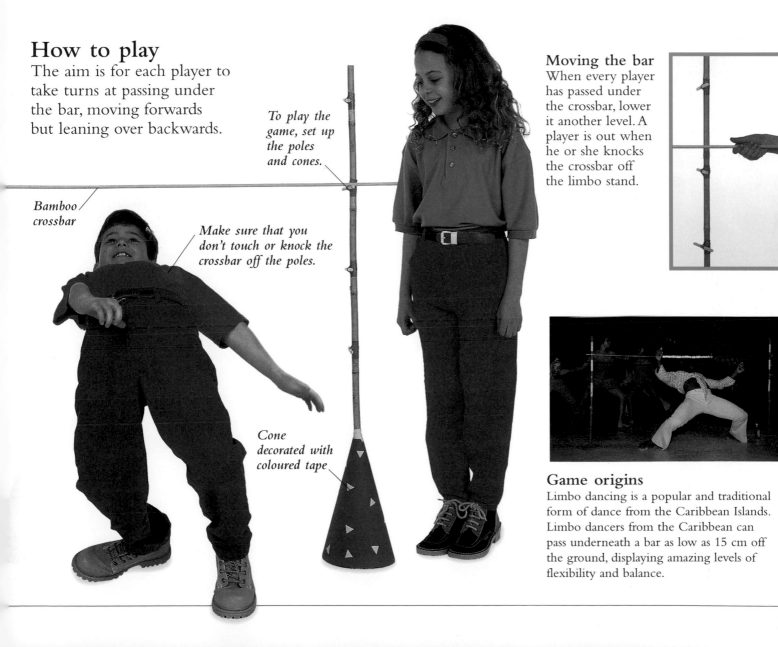

How to play

The aim is for each player to take turns at passing under the bar, moving forwards but leaning over backwards.

To play the game, set up the poles and cones.

Bamboo crossbar

Make sure that you don't touch or knock the crossbar off the poles.

Cone decorated with coloured tape

Moving the bar

When every player has passed under the crossbar, lower it another level. A player is out when he or she knocks the crossbar off the limbo stand.

Game origins

Limbo dancing is a popular and traditional form of dance from the Caribbean Islands. Limbo dancers from the Caribbean can pass underneath a bar as low as 15 cm off the ground, displaying amazing levels of flexibility and balance.

TUG OF WAR

Here is an Eskimo game for two players sitting on the ground. Tug-of-War games are a show of strength and often represent the struggle between two opposites, such as good and evil, or hot and cold.

You will need

2 wooden poles 35 cm long

EQUIPMENT

Scissors

1.5 metres of rope

Coloured tape

Making the handles

Decorate the ends of the handles with tape. Leaving 50 cm of rope between the handles, loop the rope around the handles and tie it in a knot.

GOLDEN GATE

In this traditional game from the Czech Republic for six or more players, good and evil do battle in a Tug of War.

The other players line up and pass under the gateway singing a rhyme.

1 Two players secretly choose to be either an angel or a devil. These players join hands and make an arch.

Lowered gate

2 When the gate is lowered, the trapped player chooses a side and stands beside the player. The next trapped player stands beside the opposite player. This continues until each player is on a team.

Grasp the rope and lean back.

How to play

Two players, roughly the same height, sit opposite each other with their feet touching. Each player grips a handle and pulls until the rope is taut. On the word "Go!", both players tug on the handles trying to pull the other player over.

Keep your arms straight.

Grip the handles tightly.

Game origins

In Northern Canada, Tug of War is played to predict how cold winter will be. One team consists of people born in winter, the other of people born in summer – if summer wins it will be a warm winter.

How to play

Each team, selected secretly for the good or the evil side, must have an equal number of players. The team that pulls the other team over the mark to their side wins the war.

Grip the rope with both hands.

3 Draw a mark on the ground. The angel and the devil then reveal their identity and the Tug of War begins. Each team takes hold of the rope and, on the word "Go!", pulls hard, trying to get the other team to fall over the mark.

Line between the two teams

Place your feet wide apart for a steady base.

185

KICK THE BIRD

Kick the Bird is an action game from Korea that is not as nasty as it sounds! The soft ball decorated like a bird can be made with any filling, from sawdust to lentils. Practise the different ways you can keep the bird off the ground without using your hands. Play this on your own or with a friend.

You will need

Coloured felt

Coloured sock

Lentils or beans

Strong glue

Spoon

Coloured feathers

EQUIPMENT

Scissors

Pen

Ruler

Making the bird

1 Ask an adult to hold a sock open for you and carefully fill it to the heel with the lentils to form a ball. Tie the sock firmly in a tight knot.

2 Cut two eyes and a beak out of felt. Glue these on to the sock to make a face. Cut out decorations for the sock tail and feet and glue them on.

3 Glue the ends of the coloured feathers before pushing them carefully into the sock for wings. Let the bird dry fully before using it.

The finished bird

The bird is a ball to kick with a face, tail, feet, and feathers.

Feathers pushed in to the sock for wings

Decorated sock end for a tail

Beak made from a double layer of felt

Game Origins

Korea is a country neighboured by China and Japan. Soldiers in Korea play this game as a means of making them quick witted. In cold weather, children find it a good way of keeping their feet warm.

How to play

The aim of Kick the Bird is to keep the bird in the air for as long as possible without using your hands.

Between two players

Kick the bird between two players, seeing how long you can keep going before the bird falls.

Head butt

As the bird comes down, try hitting it with your forehead or the top of your head.

Knee kick

Drop the bird on to your knee and bounce it up in the air. Remember to keep your balance on your other leg.

Heel kick

Try to keep the bird off the ground by kicking it with the heel, front, or side of your foot.

SWING BALL

Ghana is a hot country on the west coast of Africa. Here children play Swing Ball, a game for two players, outside in the sun. The ball and rope also detach from the pole to become a jumping game for two or more people.

EQUIPMENT

Spoon

Scissors

Making the ball

1 Cut off one leg of the tights. Fill the toe with lentils. Tie it closed with thread before twisting the end and wrapping it back over the ball.

You will need

For the pole

2 wooden rings

Coloured tape

Strong glue

Pole 2 metres long

For the ball

1.5 metres of cord

Thread

A pair of tights

250 g of lentils

Jump Ball

Several players form a circle round one player who holds the rope and swings the ball round in a circle, 30 cm from the ground. When players are hit by the rope, they are out of the game.

Players jump the rope as it swings round in a circle.

Detach the rope from the pole

Making the pole

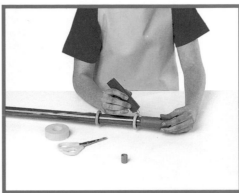

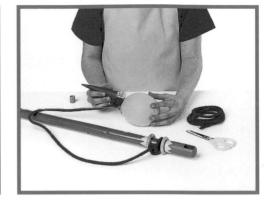

2 Now the soft ball has two outer
layers to make it strong. To finish
the ball, securely tie the open end
with another length of thread.

1 Slide the two wooden rings on
to the pole. Leave a 5 cm gap
between the rings. Carefully glue
them in place at the top of the pole.

2 Tie the cord securely to the ball.
Tie the other end of the cord to
the pole between the two wooden
rings. Decorate the pole with tape.

How to play
The aim of the game
is to swing the ball in
one direction so that it
wraps around the pole.

*The rope
swings in a
circle around
the pole with
the soft ball
attached.*

1 Players stand opposite
each other on either side
of the pole. One player hits
the ball anti-clockwise with
his or her hand and the other
player hits the ball clockwise.

2 Take turns at
hitting the ball so
that you get the rope
to spiral right round
the pole towards you.

*If you hit the
ball and it
wraps around
the pole, you
score one point.*

Game origins
Some children in Ghana have
to walk a long way to get to
school. Swing Ball is a popular
game as it can be played
outside and uses bits and
pieces found in the home.

SKIPPING

Children everywhere have skipped rope for centuries, often chanting rhymes as they skip. Start with forward and backward skipping before moving on to more complicated steps.

You will need

Long skipping rope

Short skipping rope

Swing the rope up over your head and down in front of you.

Hold one rope handle in each hand.

Forward skipping
This is the easiest form of skipping. Jump or skip over the rope in a regular rhythm as it touches the ground.

Backward skipping
Start with the rope in front of your feet. Swing it up in front of you and over your head.

Jump with your feet together.

Trick skipping

For single skipping, the ideal length of rope should stretch from one shoulder, under your feet, and up to the other shoulder. Here are some fun skipping tricks to master.

Swing the rope to one side then the other, with a skip in between.

Cross your arms to make a loop to skip through

Boxercise skipping
Complete one forward skip, then pass the rope to one side and swing it in a circle.

Cross-arm skipping
Start with a forward skip. Cross your arms in front of you as the rope comes over your head, and skip through the loop formed by the rope. Follow this with another forward step.

Double skipping
This rope is long enough for two players to skip together. Make up a sequence of steps to follow, or skip along to a chant.

Swing the rope together to form an even curve for the skippers to jump over.

Skipping in pairs
One player starts skipping. A second player jumps in to join the first player and they skip together.

Jump at the same time to allow the rope to keep moving.

One player skips backwards and the other player skips forwards.

Advanced skipping
Another way to skip in a pair, is to have one player turn one end of the rope and one player jump, as shown.

Turn the rope and jump at the same time.

Jump over the rope when it hits the ground.

Grip the rope with one hand.

Group skipping
Two players, who are the rope holders, take one end of the rope each and turn it continuously. The remaining players are the skippers. Each skipper runs in, completes a number of jumps, and runs out before the next skipper jumps in.

Game origins
Skipping is an excellent way to keep fit and is good training for athletes. These American children are performing a form of skipping called Double Dutch. This involves turning two ropes at the same time, and players require great concentration and coordination as they jump both ropes.

HOPSCOTCH

Hopscotch, a game for any number of people, is played all over the world. There are many variations of hopscotch, but most hopscotch games involve hopping along a numbered board chalked on the ground and picking up stones.

You will need

Coloured chalk   *Stones*

Hopscotch board

The squares on a hopscotch board should be big enough to give you enough room to hop inside.

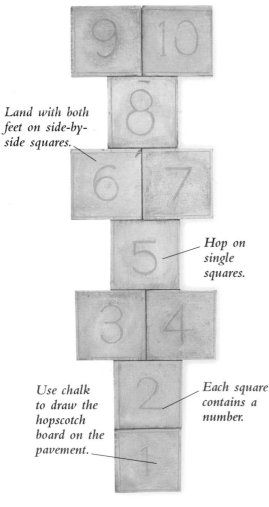

Land with both feet on side-by-side squares.

Hop on single squares.

Use chalk to draw the hopscotch board on the pavement.

Each square contains a number.

How to play

To make a hopscotch board, scratch the outline on firm dry earth, or draw it in chalk on a playground or pavement.

1 The first player throws a stone into square 1. If the stone does not land inside the correct square, it becomes the next player's turn.

The stone must land inside the correct square.

Always hop over the square with the stone in it.

5 If you lose your balance or throw the stone into the wrong square, it becomes the next player's turn. When it's your turn again start from the point where you went wrong. The winner is the first player to complete the hopscotch up to square 10.

If one player overbalances, the next player takes a turn.

One foot lands on each side-by-side square.

2 Carefully hop over square 1 containing the stone and into square 2. Then continue down the board.

3 At the end of the board jump on numbers 9 and 10. Now jump around and return down the board to hop on to square 2.

Jump to face the other direction at the end.

4 Balancing on one foot in square 2, pick up the stone and then hop into square 1 and off the board. On each turn, throw the stone into the next square.

Pick up the stone on the return journey.

Jump over square 5 and into squares 6 and 7.

On the return trip, balance in square 6 and pick up the stone.

Alternative hopscotch games

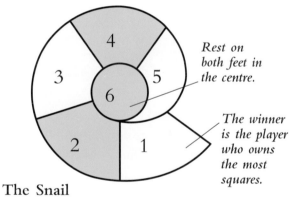

Rest on both feet in the centre.

The winner is the player who owns the most squares.

The Snail
A player hops to the centre of the board on one foot and back again. The player writes his or her name on a square. Only the owner can hop on to a named square. The game ends when all squares are owned and no one can hop to the centre.

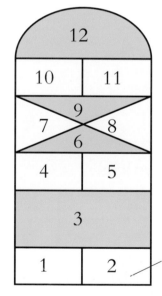

The Pilgrim
A player kicks a stone into square 1 with his or her hopping foot, and hops into square 1. Then the player kicks the stone into square 2, then hops into square 2, and so on. A player whose foot or stone misses a square or touches a line is out.

Play continues in rounds until only one player remains.

When you reach the end of the board, jump around on both feet and hop back.

DROP THE HANKIE

Here's a simple game of bluff from India, called Dhamal Dhoko. By pretending to drop a hankie behind each player in a circle you create an exciting guessing game. This game can be played indoors or outside, with six or more players.

You will need

Thread

Marble

Handkerchief

EQUIPMENT

Scissors

Making the hankie

Cut off a length of thread. Place the marble in the centre of the handkerchief. Tie the thread securely around the marble so that it doesn't fall out.

How to play

To start the game one player is chosen to be the bluffer. The rest of the players sit on the ground in a circle facing inwards.

1 The bluffer holds the hankie and walks round the outside of the circle, pretending to drop the hankie behind each sitter.

2 When the hankie has been dropped, the bluffer carries on walking and bluffing, aiming to get right round the circle before the hankie has been discovered.

Game origins

With 800 million people living in India, there are many children to play drop the hankie, which is a simple name for entertaining large groups. The Taj Mahal, the symbol of India, was built for the Emperor's wife, who had a big family.

4 For the chaser to catch the bluffer, he or she must tap the bluffer on the back with the hankie. The chaser then returns to his or her space in the circle and the bluffer continues the game.

Chaser tapping the bluffer with the dropped hankie

Double bluff
If the bluffer makes it around the circle undetected, the bluffer picks up the dropped hankie, taps the sitter with it on the back, and the two change places.

3 A sitter who feels the hankie behind them picks it up, and then chases the bluffer. The bluffer tries to escape the chaser by running round the circle and sitting down in the empty space before being caught.

The sitters are not allowed to look behind them to see if the hankie is there – they must feel for the hankie instead.

RACING GAMES

Here are some traditional games from around the world for any number of people to play at parties, in the garden, or in the playground.

Grip your partner's legs firmly so that you don't drop them.

Wheelbarrow Race

Players form pairs. One player holds the legs of his or her partner and lifts them up. First practise moving forward together. To race other pairs, start at the word "Go!" and rush to the finishing line.

Keep your back straight so that you don't collapse!

Keep your arms straight and 'walk' forward on your hands.

On the word "Go!", run up to the crouching player.

Sack Race

This game was originally played in potato sacks, but you can use old pillowcases instead. Each player steps inside a pillowcase and lines up at the race starting line and must hop to the finish.

You will need

The first player across the finishing line is the winner.

On the word "Go!", each person has to hop to the finish.

Hold the pillowcase firmly at the top.

It is easy to fall over, so keep your balance by landing on both feet.

Place a foot in each corner of the case.

A large pillowcase per person

Leapfrog Race

Players form pairs and decide how many leaps are in the race. One player in each pair runs five paces and crouches into a frog. The second player runs up, places his or her hands on the frog's back, and leaps over.

Keep your head well tucked in.

Bend down with your hands gripping your ankles.

Place both hands firmly on the frog's back.

Continue the race

The second player then runs forward and crouches down into the frog position and the first player leaps over.

The winners are the first players to complete the leaps.

Keep your arms out for balance.

Land safely and solidly with both feet apart.

The higher you leap, the further you will travel.

Hold on to the carrier's shoulders and sit on his or her hips.

Hold on tight to the rider's legs.

On the word "Go!", the pairs run as fast as they can to the finishing line.

Use a bag or cone as a finishing line marker.

Piggyback Race

Players form pairs. The lighter player climbs on to the stronger person's back and they line up at the start. If a pair collapses, they go back to the start.

CATTLE STOCKADE

Here's a game played by children in Botswana, a country in Africa. The name of the game comes from the 2.5 million cattle that are farmed in the country and which are an important source of food. Cattle Stockade is a rowdy game for six or more players that can be played indoors or outside.

How to play

A group of four or more people link hands to form a fence or stockade and try to prevent the bull from escaping.

1 Players choose one person to be the bull in the centre of the circle. The remaining players link hands and form the stockade.

One person volunteers to be the bull.

Bend down to prevent the bull from crawling under the stockade.

Game origins

Farmers in Botswana allow their herds of cattle to roam and graze the grasslands. The cattle are rounded up into stockades when they need to be branded or sold.

2 The bull then tries to escape from the stockade by crawling under or leaping over the arms of the other players. The stockade tries to stop the bull escaping without letting go of each other's hands.

Linking hands
To form a strong stockade players should link hands tightly, as shown.

Cattle stampede!
A large group of players can make the game more challenging by adding more cattle to the stockade.

The bull tries to escape the stockade.

3 Once the bull has escaped, he or she can join the stockade and choose another player to be the bull.

Another way for the bull to escape is by stepping over the linked arms of the stockade.

FINGER PUPPETS

You can make a cheerful handful of finger puppets using the template shown on page 237. Make the puppets from brightly coloured felt or from any scraps of fabric or paper you can find. Try the animal puppets shown here or invent some of your own.

You will need

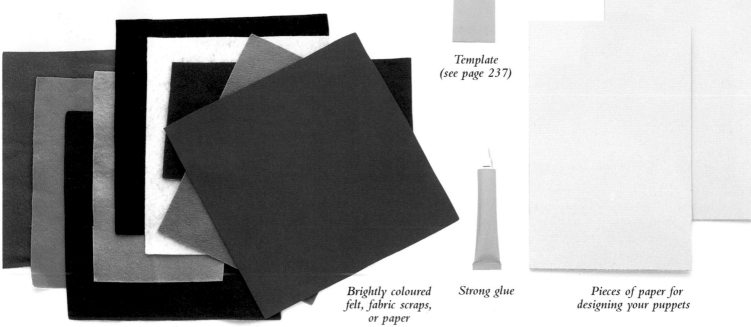

Template (see page 237)

Brightly coloured felt, fabric scraps, or paper

Strong glue

Pieces of paper for designing your puppets

What to do

1 Draw your designs for puppets on paper before you make them. Look at pictures of animals or people to get some ideas and then simplify them.

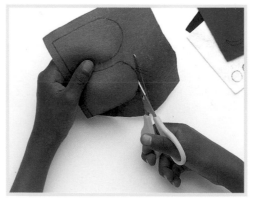

2 Lay the body template on a piece of felt and draw around it twice. Draw the puppet features on other pieces of felt. Cut out the body pieces.

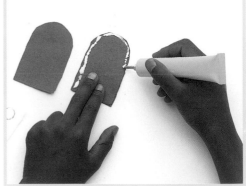

3 Spread a fine line of glue around the curved edge of one piece of the body, leaving the bottom edge free. Press the two body pieces together.

Cheerful puppets

You could make a whole troupe of smiling animals like these, or a collection of characters from fairy tales. Your puppets will work best if they are simple and brightly coloured. Why not make up a play for the puppets with a friend!

Put the puppet on your index finger.

4 Now carefully cut out the puppet's features that you drew on the other pieces of felt. Remember to cut out two arms, two legs, etc.

5 Arrange the cut-out features on the body to see how they look. If any part doesn't look quite right, try making another version of it.

6 First glue the legs and arms (or wings and paws) to the back of the body. Then glue the rest of the animal's features on to the front.

Mouse

Owl

Lion

Panda

Cockerel

Frog

Parrot

Pig

Moving the puppets
Make the puppets look as though they are talking by moving your fingers.

Curl your other fingers and thumb away from the puppet.

The paws are glued to inside of the puppet's body.

SHADOW PUPPETS

Putting on a shadow play with your friends
is a great way to spend a rainy afternoon.
Here you can find out how to make brightly
coloured shadow puppets with moving joints.
Turn the page to find out how to make the
shadow theatre and how to work the puppets
and put on a fantastic show.

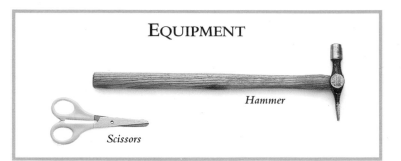

EQUIPMENT

Hammer

Scissors

You will need

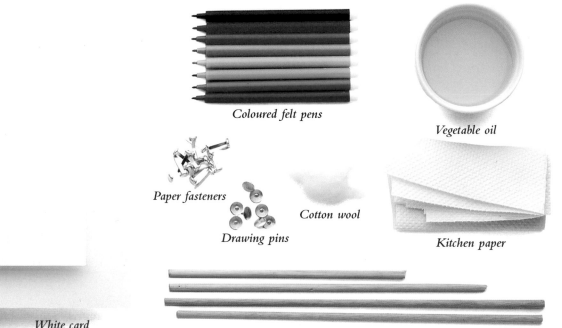

Coloured felt pens

Vegetable oil

Paper fasteners

Cotton wool

Drawing pins

Kitchen paper

White card

2 or 3 pieces of dowelling about 30 cm long for each puppet

Making a puppet

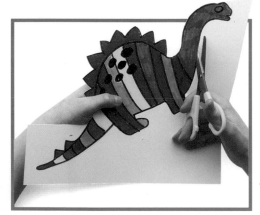

1 Draw the puppet you want to
make on white card with a black
felt pen. Keep the shape simple and
add details such as stripes or spots.

2 Colour in the puppet with felt
pens. The brighter the colours,
the better the puppet will look in the
theatre. Then cut it out carefully.

3 Next, cut off any part of the
puppet that you want to be able
to move. This puppet will have a
neck that can move up and down.

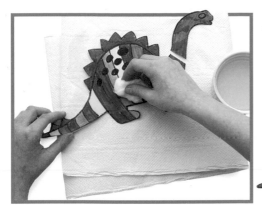

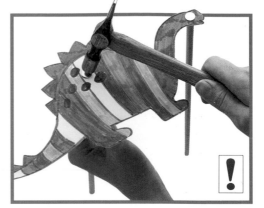

4 Lay the puppet on some kitchen paper and dab it all over with cotton wool soaked in vegetable oil. Do this to both sides of each puppet.

5 Make holes with a drawing pin in the parts of the puppet you want to join. Push a paper fastener through each hole and fold the legs open.

6 Then ask an adult to join a dowel stick to both parts of the puppet by hammering a drawing pin into the end of a stick, as shown.

Puppet world

Here are some ideas for shadow puppets and scenery for the theatre. Copy these, or make puppets of characters from your favourite stories.

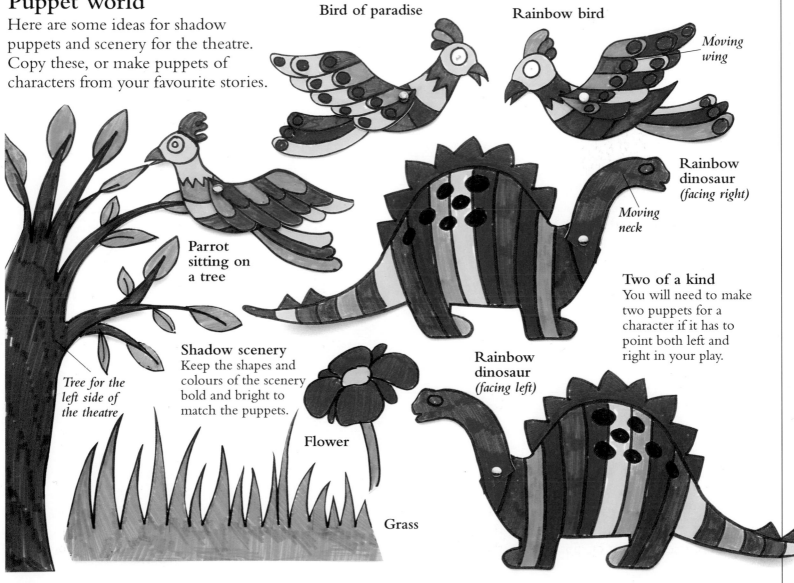

Bird of paradise

Rainbow bird

Moving wing

Parrot sitting on a tree

Tree for the left side of the theatre

Shadow scenery Keep the shapes and colours of the scenery bold and bright to match the puppets.

Flower

Grass

Rainbow dinosaur *(facing right)*

Moving neck

Two of a kind You will need to make two puppets for a character if it has to point both left and right in your play.

Rainbow dinosaur *(facing left)*

WORLD IN A THEATRE

To bring the puppets to life, stand the theatre on a table near a bright light, such as a lamp, so that light shines in through the back of the box and on to the puppets and the screen. Make up a simple story and then you are ready to rehearse. You will need to ask a friend to help you, as two hands are needed to work each puppet.

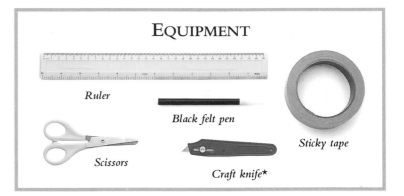

EQUIPMENT

Ruler

Black felt pen

Scissors

Craft knife★

Sticky tape

You will need

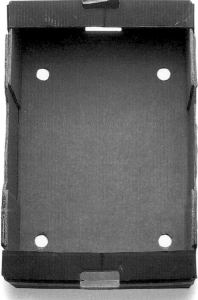

A strong, rectangular cardboard box

Coloured paper for decorating the theatre

Glue stick　　*Tracing paper or greaseproof paper*

Making the theatre

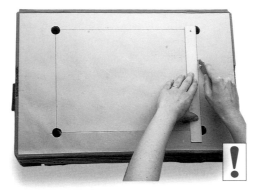

1 Measure and draw a rectangle on the bottom of the cardboard box, as shown. Then ask an adult to cut it out of the box with a craft knife.

2 Cut out a rectangle of tracing paper a little bigger than the hole in the box. Tape the sides of the paper down over the hole inside the box.

3 Tape the pieces of scenery you have made, such as trees, flowers, and grass, coloured-side down on to the paper screen inside the box.

4 Turn the box over. Cut out shapes from coloured paper and glue them round the edge of the screen, to make the box look like a real theatre.

★Ask an adult for help when using a craft knife.

Make the bird fly by moving its wing up and down.

Slide the puppet across the screen as you move its wing.

Moving puppets

You will need both hands to make each puppet move, one for each stick. To bring a puppet to life, slide it along the back of the screen while moving the sticks.

Behind the scenes

When you are ready to perform your play, stand to one side, behind the screen.

Move your arm up and down to move the dinosaur's head.

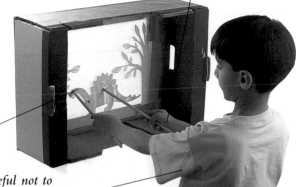

Hold one puppet stick in each hand.

Be careful not to block out the light from your light source.

Decorate the front of the theatre with coloured paper shapes.

Rainbow dinosaur

Stick the scenery to the sides of the theatre.

JUNK MODELS

You do not need expensive materials or kits to make exciting models. Here you can learn how to make toy binoculars, a truck, a robot, and an impressive castle – all from everyday rubbish that you would normally just throw away. Turn the page to find out how to put the finishing touches to the models.

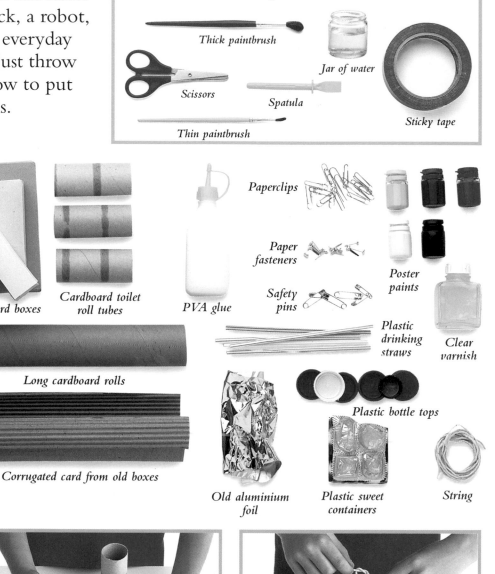

EQUIPMENT

Thick paintbrush

Jar of water

Scissors

Spatula

Thin paintbrush

Sticky tape

You will need

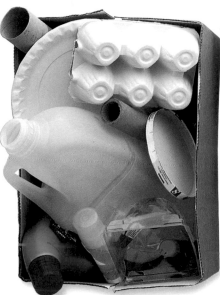

Empty cartons, tubes, and packets

Cardboard boxes

Cardboard toilet roll tubes

Long cardboard rolls

Corrugated card from old boxes

PVA glue

Paperclips

Paper fasteners

Safety pins

Poster paints

Plastic drinking straws

Clear varnish

Old aluminium foil

Plastic sweet containers

Plastic bottle tops

String

Making binoculars

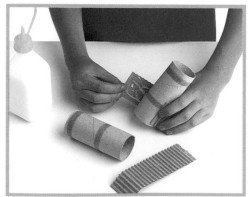

1 Cut two strips of corrugated card 5 cm wide and long enough to wrap round a toilet-roll tube. Glue one round the end of each tube.

2 Draw round a tube four times on corrugated card and cut out the four circles. Glue them together between the two tubes, as shown.

3 Ask an adult to make a hole in each tube. Thread a piece of string through the holes, and tie a knot in each end, as shown.

Making the truck

1 Find two boxes and a lid like these. Draw windows on the front and sides of the larger box and cut them out. This will be the cab of the truck.

2 Glue the box lid and the two boxes together on top of a piece of card. Glue three small tubes underneath the truck for the wheels.

3 Push plastic bottle tops into the ends of the tubes to complete the wheels. Then paint the truck with brightly coloured poster paints.

Making the castle

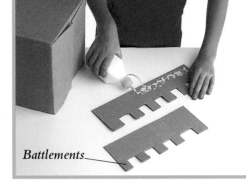

Battlements

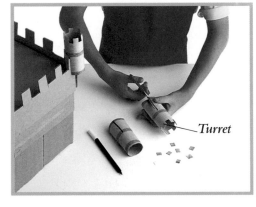

Turret

1 Find a large square box for the base of the castle. Cut four strips of card, each the same length as a side of the box. Cut battlements along them.

2 Spread glue along the base of each strip of battlements and glue them around the base of the box, as shown, so that the battlements stick up.

3 For turrets, cut battlements at the tops of four small tubes. Cut two slits in each tube and slot them on to the four corners of the castle.

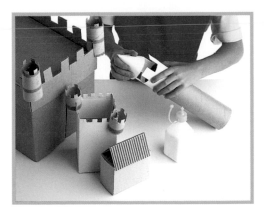

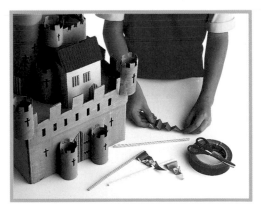

4 Use a long tube for a tall tower. Cut battlements in a strip of paper and glue it around the top. Then glue on a cone of paper for the roof.

5 Make small buildings for the castle from smaller boxes. Use corrugated card to make roofs, windows, and doors. Then paint the buildings.

6 Glue all the bits of the castle together. Paint it, adding crosses for windows. Make flags from folded paper triangles and tape them to straws.

CARDBOARD CREATIONS

Making the robot

Here are some of the models you can create. The truck and binoculars only take an hour or so to make. The robot takes a bit longer, and the castle at least an afternoon. The models you make will look different, depending on the boxes and bits of junk you use. Have fun experimenting!

1 Attach small tube arms to the box body with paper fasteners. Ask an adult to make a hole first, then push the fasteners through and fold open the legs.

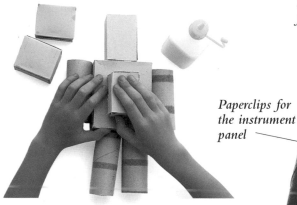

2 Glue the rest of the boxes together, as shown. Use two small tubes for the legs and small boxes for the head, feet, and chest.

3 Paint the robot and leave it to dry. Then coat with clear varnish. When the varnish is dry, add details for the face, hands, uniform, and instrument panel.

Plastic lid for a hat

Pieces of egg box covered in foil for ears

Sweet case for a mask

Safety-pin mouth

Small box for the head

Foil-covered bottle tops for epaulettes

Paperclips for the instrument panel

Small cardboard-tube arm

Foil-covered bottle top for a hand

Gold press-studs for buttons

Robot captain
The basic robot is made up of one large box and four smaller boxes, with cardboard tubes for arms and legs. Paint your robot a bright colour, then add shiny details with paperclips, press-studs, and foil-covered bottle tops.

Cardboard tubes for legs

Small boxes for feet

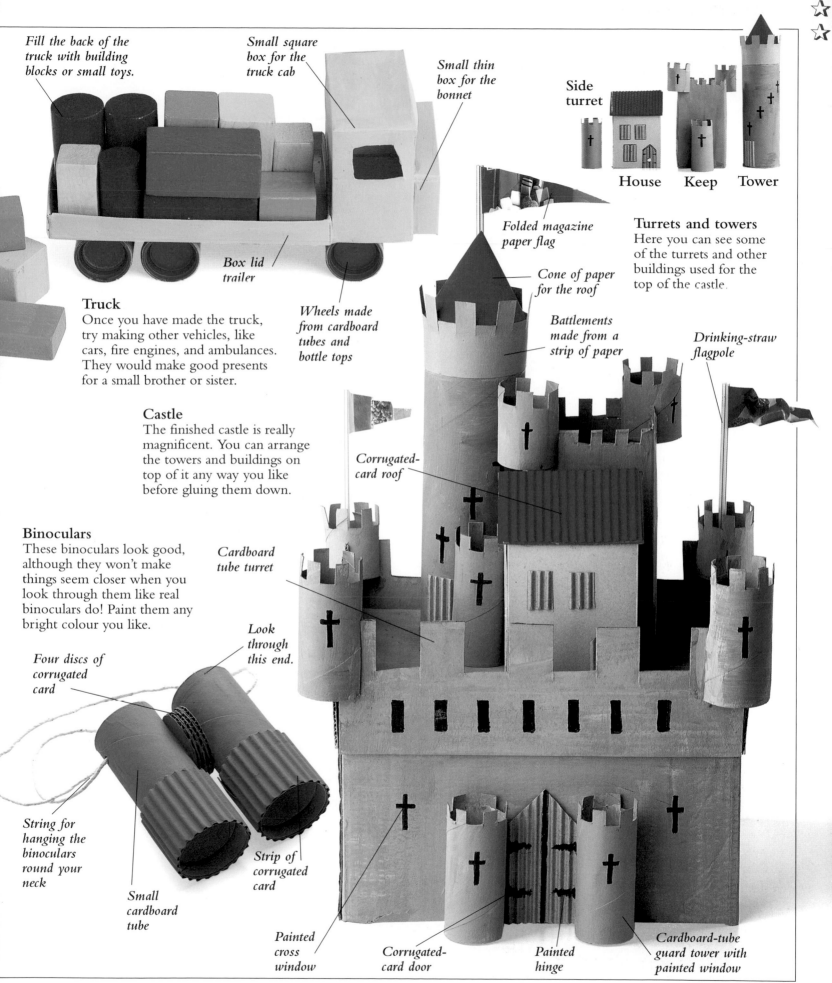

Fill the back of the truck with building blocks or small toys.

Small square box for the truck cab

Small thin box for the bonnet

Side turret

House   Keep   Tower

Folded magazine paper flag

Turrets and towers

Here you can see some of the turrets and other buildings used for the top of the castle.

Cone of paper for the roof

Battlements made from a strip of paper

Drinking-straw flagpole

Box lid trailer

Wheels made from cardboard tubes and bottle tops

Truck

Once you have made the truck, try making other vehicles, like cars, fire engines, and ambulances. They would make good presents for a small brother or sister.

Castle

The finished castle is really magnificent. You can arrange the towers and buildings on top of it any way you like before gluing them down.

Corrugated-card roof

Binoculars

These binoculars look good, although they won't make things seem closer when you look through them like real binoculars do! Paint them any bright colour you like.

Cardboard tube turret

Four discs of corrugated card

Look through this end.

String for hanging the binoculars round your neck

Small cardboard tube

Strip of corrugated card

Painted cross window

Corrugated-card door

Painted hinge

Cardboard-tube guard tower with painted window

HOLIDAY SOUVENIRS

Instead of hiding your holiday photographs and souvenirs in a box, you can use them as the starting point for more lasting treasures. By creating your own personal travel diary or phrase book, or by mounting your photographs and giving them decorative frames, you can enjoy your souvenirs all year round.

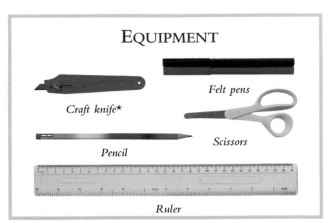

EQUIPMENT

Craft knife★

Pencil

Felt pens

Scissors

Ruler

You will need

For all projects

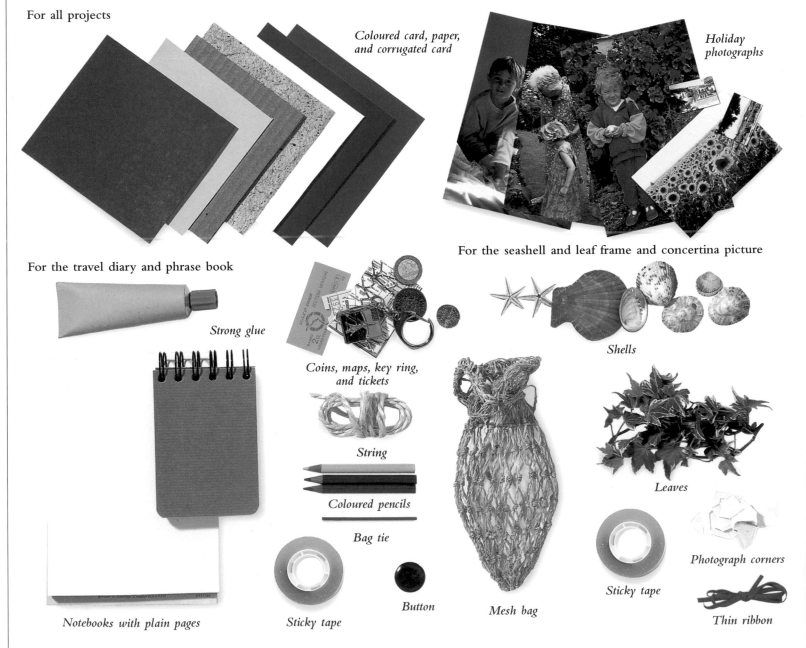

Coloured card, paper, and corrugated card

Holiday photographs

For the travel diary and phrase book

Strong glue

Coins, maps, key ring, and tickets

For the seashell and leaf frame and concertina picture

Shells

String

Leaves

Coloured pencils

Bag tie

Notebooks with plain pages

Sticky tape

Button

Mesh bag

Photograph corners

Sticky tape

Thin ribbon

Travel diary

1 For a travel diary cover that looks like the flag of a country you have visited, glue pieces of coloured paper to the cover of a notebook.

2 Thread a button on to a bag tie. Make a hole near the edge of the front cover. Thread the tie through it and tape the ends down.

3 Make two small holes in the back cover. Cut some string and thread it through the holes to form a loop. Tie them on the inside of the cover.

Seashell frame

1 Draw and cut out a card mount 3 cm wide, with the centre hole a little smaller than a chosen photo. Tape the photo to the back of the mount.

2 Measure and cut a frame 5 cm★ wide out of thick card. The hole in the middle should be 1 cm bigger than the mount all the way round .

3 Glue textured paper on to the frame to cover it. Glue string mesh on top of this and string around the edge. Decorate with shells on top.

Photograph collage

4 Tape the mount to the frame. Cut out some corrugated card the same size as the frame. Glue it to the back of the frame as a backing board.

1 Cut out a rectangle of card. Cut four evenly spaced rectangles out of it. Trim the photos and tape them, face up, to the back of the mount.

2 Glue the mount on to thick backing card. Make a frame bigger than the mount, glue some leaves on it, and tape it to the corners of the mount.

WORDS AND PICTURES

Concertina picture

1 For four 10 cm x 15 cm photos, cut out a piece of card 19 cm x 56 cm. Score a vertical line every 14 cm. Fold the card along the lines.

2 Cut a slot at each side of the card. Tie and knot ribbons through the slots. Slip photo corners on the photos and glue the corners to the card.

Holiday memories

The pictures and notebooks bring back memories of many different holidays by the sea, at home in the garden, or visiting a foreign country. You can adapt any of these ideas to suit your own particular holiday.

Red mount card

Frame decorated with leaves

Concertina holiday picture
When you have finished, stand the concertina card on a desk or shelf. To give this card as a present, tie the ends of the ribbon together to keep it flat.

Photograph collage
Close-up photographs work well with this mount. Decorate the frame with leaves, bark, or twigs.

Ribbon tied to slot

Photograph corner

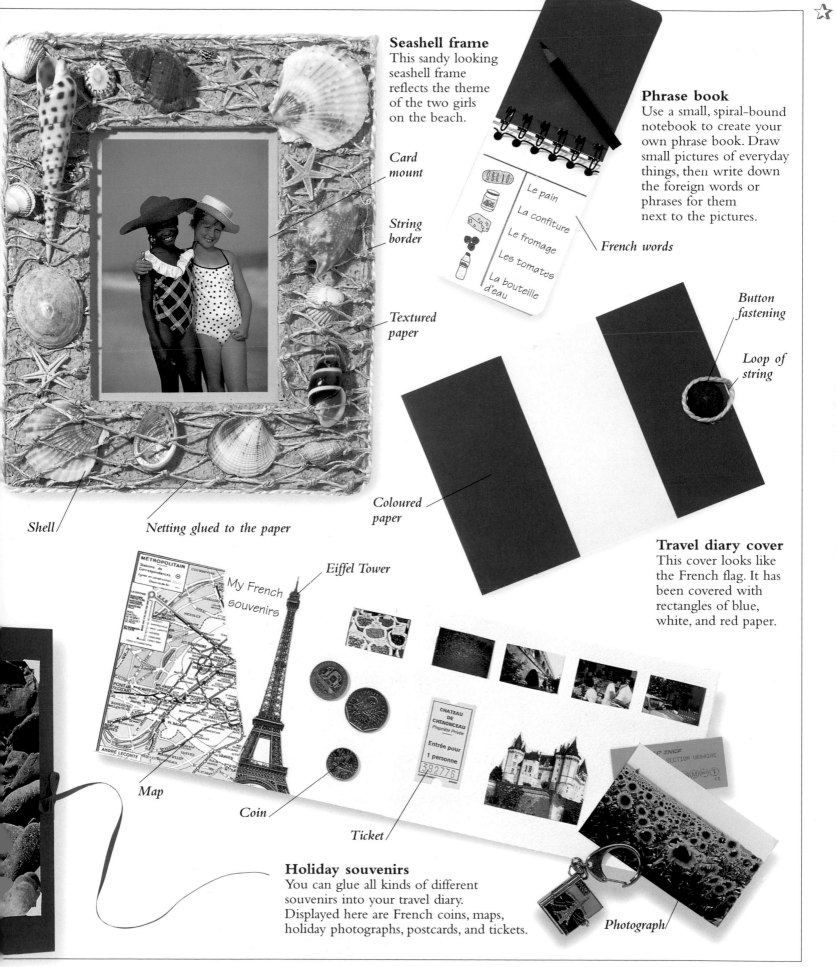

Seashell frame
This sandy looking seashell frame reflects the theme of the two girls on the beach.

Card mount

String border

Textured paper

Shell

Netting glued to the paper

Phrase book
Use a small, spiral-bound notebook to create your own phrase book. Draw small pictures of everyday things, then write down the foreign words or phrases for them next to the pictures.

Le pain
La confiture
Le fromage
Les tomates
La bouteille d'eau

French words

Button fastening

Loop of string

Coloured paper

Travel diary cover
This cover looks like the French flag. It has been covered with rectangles of blue, white, and red paper.

My French souvenirs

Eiffel Tower

MÉTROPOLITAIN

Map

Coin

CHATEAU DE CHENONCEAU
Propriété Privée
Entrée pour 1 personne
392776

Ticket

Holiday souvenirs
You can glue all kinds of different souvenirs into your travel diary. Displayed here are French coins, maps, holiday photographs, postcards, and tickets.

Photograph

POSTCARDS HOME

Home-made postcards are fun to make and your friends and family will treasure them as holiday memories. Choose a theme based on where you are spending your holiday – by the sea, in the country, or in a city – and remember to write an interesting message on the back.

You will need

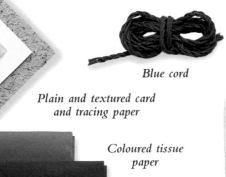

Blue cord

Plain and textured card
and tracing paper

Coloured tissue
paper

Glue stick

Small seashells

Strong glue

String

Poster paints

Making a postcard

1 Measure and cut out pieces of plain card the size you want your postcards. Carefully draw and then paint different pictures on them.

2 If you want to make a collage, cut out one of your paintings. Make a background on another card by gluing on torn pieces of paper.

3 Glue the painting to the background card. Carefully add any final details. Leave the back of the card blank to write your message.

Postcard gallery

All these cards have a seaside theme. Some are simply painted, some have cut-out shapes, and others are collages with different things stuck on them. If you are worried about a special postcard being damaged in the post, make an envelope for it out of thick paper.

Seashell collage

This card has carefully been cut out in the shape of a crab.

Flashing lighthouse

Clawed crab

Bright yellow light

Black outline

Tasty ice cream

String glued in place

Torn tissue paper

Seaside starfish

Swirls of thick paint

Textured card

Seashell

Cord tied around the edge

String border

This card was cut out and painted.

The back of the card
Don't forget to leave the back of the card blank, with room for your message, the address that the card is going to, and a stamp.

Space for address

Lifebuoy with a view

KALEIDOSCOPE

A kaleidoscope is a very clever toy: holding it to your eye and turning it, you can watch an unending display of patterns. You will need shiny mirror board, which you can buy at an art shop or make from aluminium foil glued on to card. The kaleidoscope works best if the coloured plastic pieces are thicker than paper.

You will need

Mirror board

Transparent beads and small pieces of coloured acetate or plastic

Clear plastic (from a bag)

Tracing paper

Coloured paper

White card

Glue stick

What to do

1 Carefully cut out a piece of mirror board 12 cm x 20 cm. Measure out and score two lines along it lengthways 4 cm apart.

2 Fold the board along the lines, so the mirror is inside. Tape the two edges together. Then tape a piece of clear plastic over one end of the tube.

3 Cut a piece of mirror board 12.5 cm x 3 cm. Tape it round the tube, so that it sticks out over the plastic-covered end, as shown.

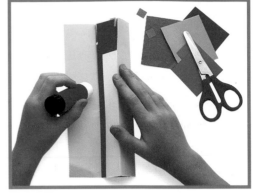

4 Hold the tube upright with the short piece of tube you have added at the top. Drop small pieces of coloured plastic and beads into it.

5 Cut out a triangular piece of tracing paper. Lay it flat over the top of the tube. Fold the edges over the tube and tape them down.

6 Cut out a piece of coloured paper 12.5 cm x 20 cm. Glue it round the tube, as shown, then decorate it with coloured paper shapes.

Pocket rainbows

Here is the finished kaleidoscope, decorated with colourful paper rectangles and squares. To make it work, face a window or a bright light and close one eye. Holding the open end of the tube up to your other eye, look into the tube and slowly turn the kaleidoscope round. Here are the sorts of patterns you may see.

As you turn the kaleidoscope round in your hands, the pattern will change before your eyes.

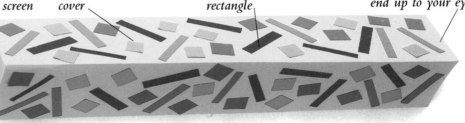

Tracing paper screen   *Yellow paper cover*   *Coloured paper rectangle*   *Hold the open end up to your eye*

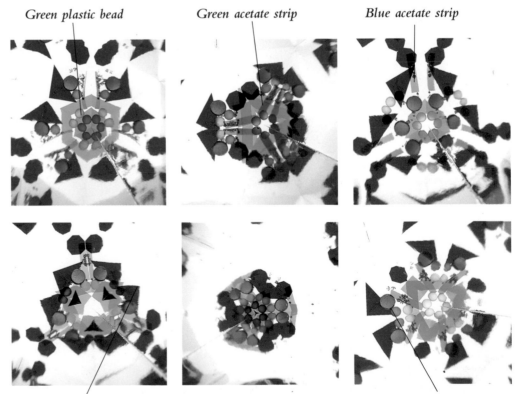

Green plastic bead   *Green acetate strip*   *Blue acetate strip*

Red acetate triangle   *Blue plastic bead*

UP PERISCOPE!

Here you can learn how to make a periscope, an amazing device for seeing things beyond your scope of vision. Periscopes were originally used on submarines to see what was above the surface of the water, but you can use one for spying on friends when they least suspect it. Use it for peeping over walls or around corners – it really works!

You will need

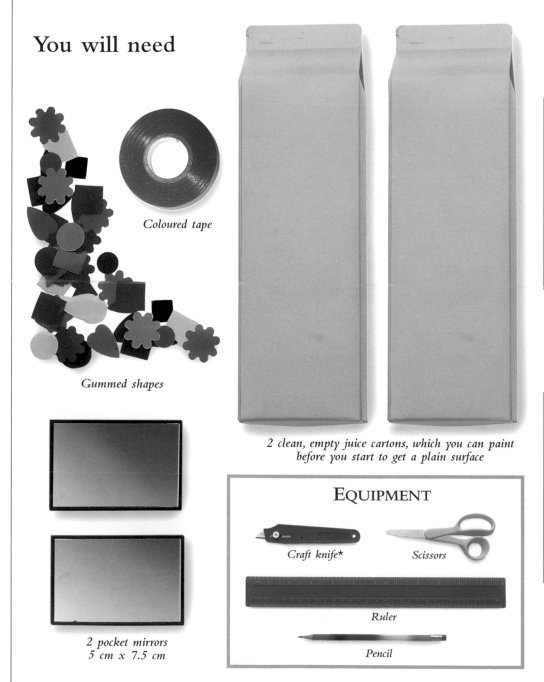

Coloured tape

Gummed shapes

*2 pocket mirrors
5 cm x 7.5 cm*

*2 clean, empty juice cartons, which you can paint
before you start to get a plain surface*

EQUIPMENT

Craft knife★

Scissors

Ruler

Pencil

Making the periscope

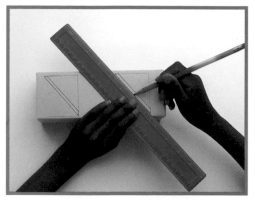

1 Cut off the carton top. Draw two right-angled triangles with 5 cm sides on one side. Draw two lines parallel to the diagonal lines, as shown.

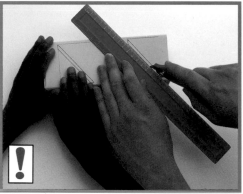

2 Ask an adult to cut out two slots along the diagonal lines using a craft knife and a ruler. Hold the carton carefully to keep it steady.

3 Turn the carton over and draw two more right-angled triangles on the opposite side. Make sure that the slots match up with the first slots.

4 Slot a pocket mirror face down through the slots at the top of the carton. Slide the second mirror into the bottom slots, face upwards.

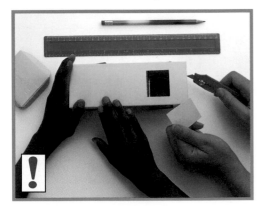

5 Draw a square on the front of the carton over the top mirror. Ask an adult to cut it out. Make a top for the carton from the base of another carton.

6 Cut out a small hole at the back of the carton over the bottom mirror. Then decorate the carton with gummed shapes.

Slot the base of the second carton into the periscope to make a new, flat lid. Decorate it in the same way as the rest of the periscope.

Top mirror facing down

Viewing window

Decorate with colourful shapes.

Tape the mirror securely in place.

Bottom mirror facing up

Reflecting images

A periscope works by reflecting an image from one mirror on to the other. A scene you cannot see over a wall is reflected in the top mirror of the periscope. This is then reflected down onto the bottom mirror. When you look through the small hole at the bottom of the periscope, you see the bottom mirror and the image that is reflected in it.

Using the periscope

You can use the periscope either by holding it upright to look over an obstacle, or by turning it sideways to see around a corner. Close one eye, hold the small hole at the bottom up to your open eye, and look through it. What can you see?

Window of periscope must be higher than the obstacle you are looking over

MAKE A KITE

Why not make your own kite with a tail and paint it in bold colours to stand out against the sky? The kite is made of thin plastic, so look out for a large, brightly coloured plastic bag or bin liner with no writing on it. To decorate the kite you will need acrylic paints or marker pens. Turn the page to see how to finish the kite and send it flying!

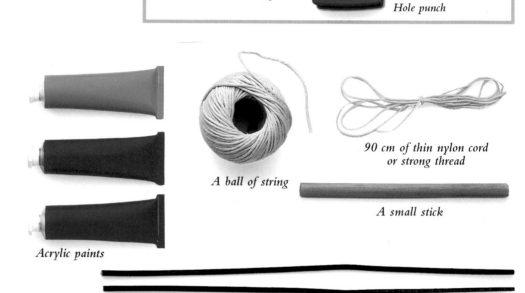

EQUIPMENT

Ruler

Scissors

Jar of water

Sticky tape

Paintbrush

Wax crayon

Craft knife★

Hole punch

You will need

A large plastic bag or bin liner

Acrylic paints

A ball of string

90 cm of thin nylon cord or strong thread

A small stick

2 garden canes, 46 cm long

What to do

1 Cut out a square of plastic, 48 cm wide. Mark the centre of the top and bottom of the square and make three marks in a line, 14 cm from the top.

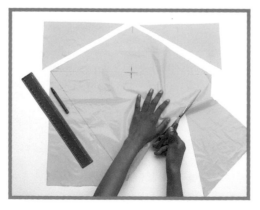

2 Draw straight lines to join up the marks at the edges of the plastic square. Cut carefully along the lines keeping the plastic flat.

3 Stick two strips of tape across all the corners of the kite, both back and front, to strengthen them. Trim the pieces of tape to fit the corners.

*Ask an adult for help when using a craft knife.

4 Fold over each corner of the kite in turn, and punch a hole through the double thickness to make two holes next to each other, as shown.

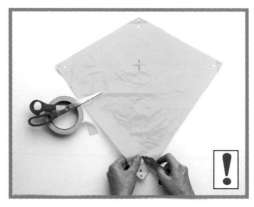

5 Stick tape strips to the centre of the kite, 11 cm from the top and 7 cm from the bottom. Ask an adult to cut a small slit in these taped patches.

6 Paint the front of the kite with acrylic paints to decorate it. Keep your design bold and simple and do not let the colours run. Leave the kite to dry.

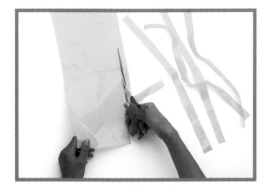

7 Cut out eight ribbons of thin plastic all the same length. Hold the ribbons together and punch a hole through one end of them.

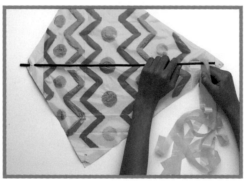

8 Push the end of one garden stick through the holes in the top of the kite. Thread the kite tail ribbons on to the other end of the stick.

9 Tape the top end of the stick in to place. Push the stick's other end through the holes at the bottom of the kite and tape it in to place too.

10 Push the ends of the second stick through the side holes in the kite. Tape it in to place in the same way, pulling the plastic tight.

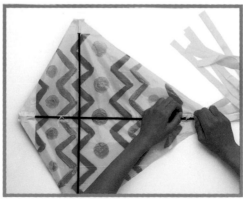

11 Thread the ends of the cord through the slits in the kite from the painted side. Knot each end on to the stick at the back of the kite.

12 Turn the kite over and tie a small loop in the cord. The loop should be directly over the top slit when you pull the cord up tight.

FLYING HIGH

Making the handle

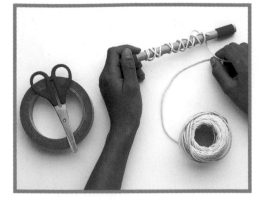  

1 Wrap sticky tape around each end of the small stick. Tie one end of the ball of string to the stick and then wind on about 30 metres of string.

2 Tie the loose end of the string through the loop in the thread at the front of the kite. Knot it twice to make sure it is secure.

Flying well
Move the position of the loop in the thread if the kite does not fly as well as you want it to.

Flying the kite

Wait for a windy day to fly your kite, then look for an open space, away from any trees, buildings, overhead cables, or roads. Ask a friend to go with you to help you to launch the kite.

Crash landings
If the kite dives and crashes, rewind most of the string before you try to launch it again.

Launching the kite
Stand with your back to the wind and unwind a few metres of the kite string. Ask your friend to carry the kite away from you, holding it up into the wind, and keeping the string pulled tight. Give the order to toss the kite up into the air. As it goes up, start letting out more string.

Keep tugging on the string to keep it tight so that the kite rises into the air.

Hold the stick at each end and keep it straight to help you control the kite.

Kite designs

You could decorate your kite with a sun design, a giant butterfly, or any ideas of your own. You could also make a multicoloured tail for it.

The looped thread is always at the front of the kite.

Kite tails
If the kite keeps nose diving, try making a longer tail for it.

The kite tail helps to keep it steady in the air.

Make sure the plastic is stretched quite tightly against the sticks to keep the kite firm.

223

SPINNING WINDMILLS

Try making these colourful paper windmills. Big windmills catch the wind in their sails to grind corn into flour, to pump water, or even to produce electricity, but these little windmills are just for fun. See how fast you can make them spin by blowing on their sails. When the weather is fine, take them outside to spin round in the wind.

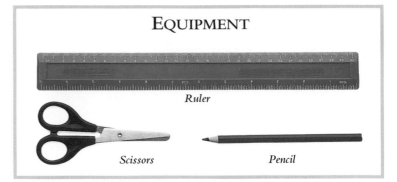

EQUIPMENT

Ruler

Scissors   *Pencil*

You will need

Pins with a large head

Small beads

Pencils with a rubber on the end

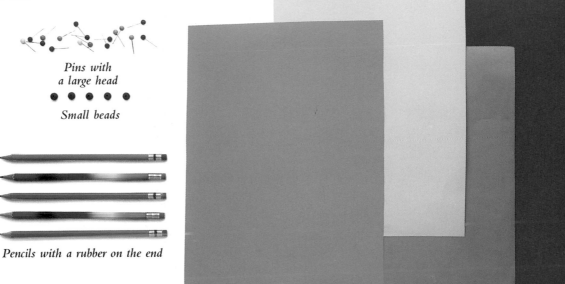

Sheets of coloured paper

What to do

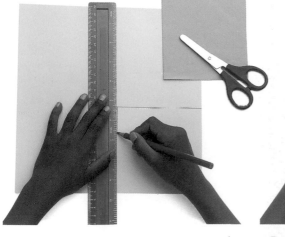

1 Using the ruler, measure out and draw two squares the same size on two different coloured pieces of paper (see page 234). Cut out the squares.

2 Using the ruler again, draw two diagonal lines across each square so they cross in the middle. Cut only two thirds of the way along each line.

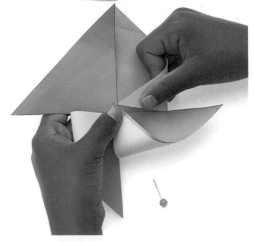

3 Hold the squares of paper together. Bend the paper back along each cut line into the centre, as shown, and hold the corners down.

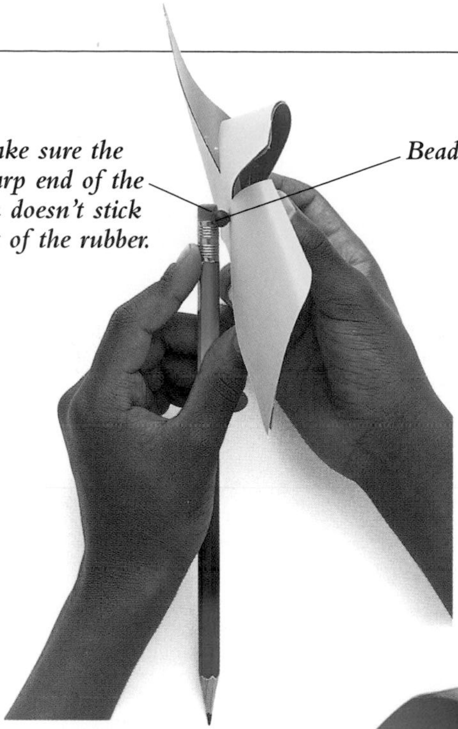

*Make sure the
sharp end of the
pin doesn't stick
out of the rubber.*

Bead

Big windmill
with red-and-
yellow sails

Blue pin

Red
pin

Rainbow
pencil
handle

Blue-and-
yellow sails

*Make sure
that the point
of your pencil
isn't sharp.*

Green-and-
yellow sails

Green pin

4 Push a pin through all
the corners of the paper
and then through a bead and into
the rubber at the end of a pencil.

5 Blow on the windmill to make it
spin. Does it work best if you
blow from the side or the front?

Test of strength
Use a windmill to test
how windy it is. The
faster the sails of your
windmill turn, the
stronger the wind is.

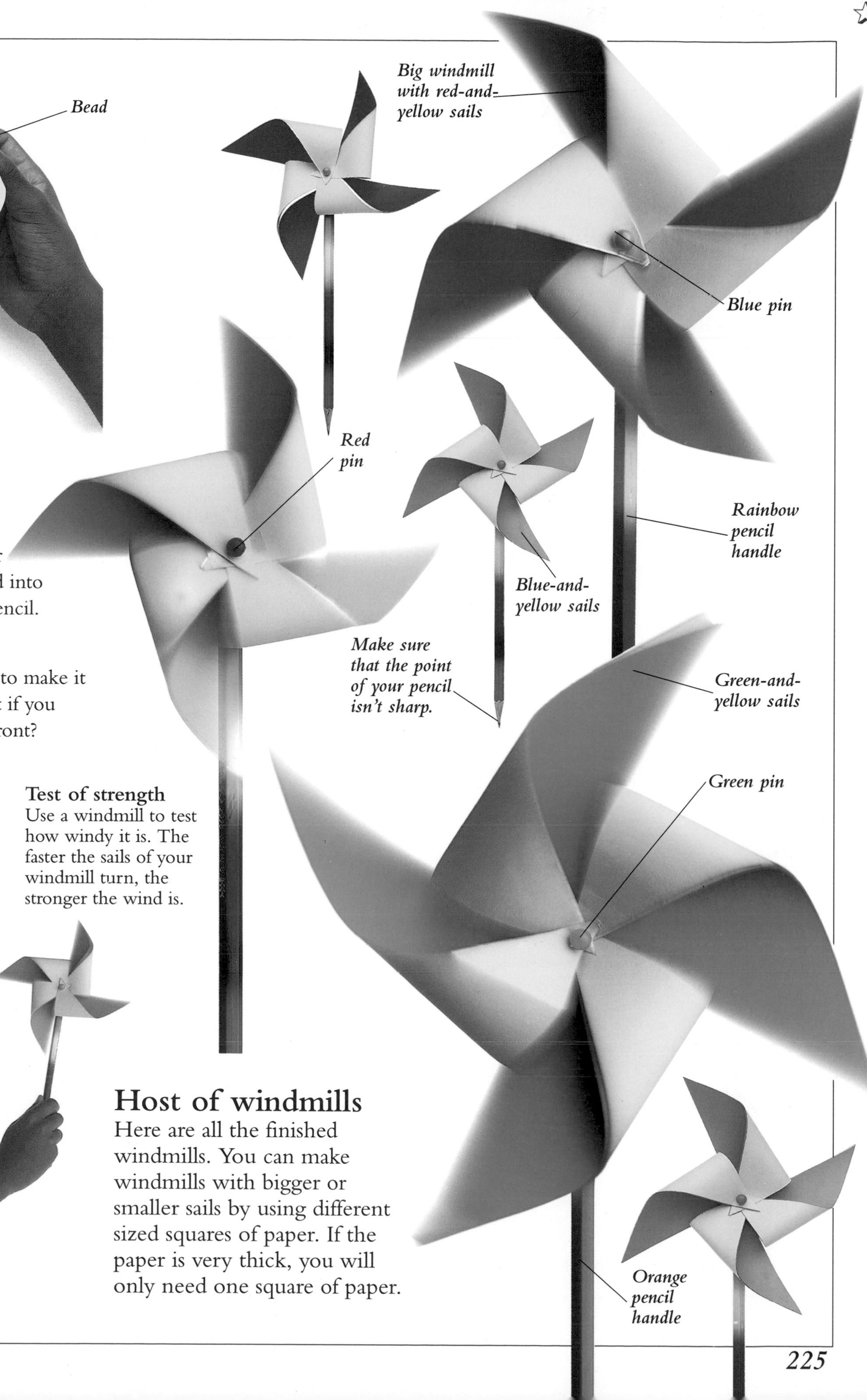

Host of windmills
Here are all the finished
windmills. You can make
windmills with bigger or
smaller sails by using different
sized squares of paper. If the
paper is very thick, you will
only need one square of paper.

Orange
pencil
handle

FLUTTERING FLAGS

Even the humblest sandcastle can look truly magnificent with its own special flag, so get out your paints and make an array of flags before going to the beach. Try making colourful hanging flags for the beach or your garden.

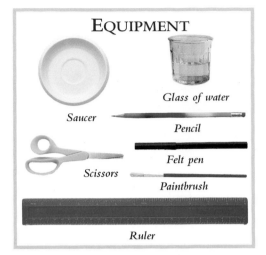
You will need

White and coloured card

Sticky tape

String

Coloured plastic bags

Gummed stars and spots

Glue stick

Poster paints

Strong glue

Plastic drinking straws and swizzle sticks

Making hanging flags

1 Using a pen and ruler, draw lots of triangles the same size on different coloured pieces of plastic. Then carefully cut out the triangles.

2 Fold the top of each triangle over a long piece of string and tape it in place. Space the triangles out along the string.

Making castle flags

1 Draw different shaped flags on card and cut them out. Paint designs on each one and stick stars or spots on some of the flags.

2 Cut out triangular shaped flags and fold them several times. Then glue the back edge of each flag to a plastic drinking straw or swizzle stick.

Hanging flags

On the beach, tie each end of the string to a deckchair, a windbreak, or garden canes so that the flags fly above the castles. At home, decorate your room with these bright flags.

String

Hanging flags made from red, blue, and yellow plastic

Flag folded to look as if it is blowing in the wind

Flags

Make many different styles of flags to create a colourful array. For one design, you could even create your own coat of arms!

Gummed spots stuck on a painted flag

Sandcastles

Make lots of little sandcastles and carefully push a flag into the top of each one. Or make a castle big enough to display all your flags together.

Plastic drinking straw

Flag painted with a cross

Swizzle stick

Gummed stars

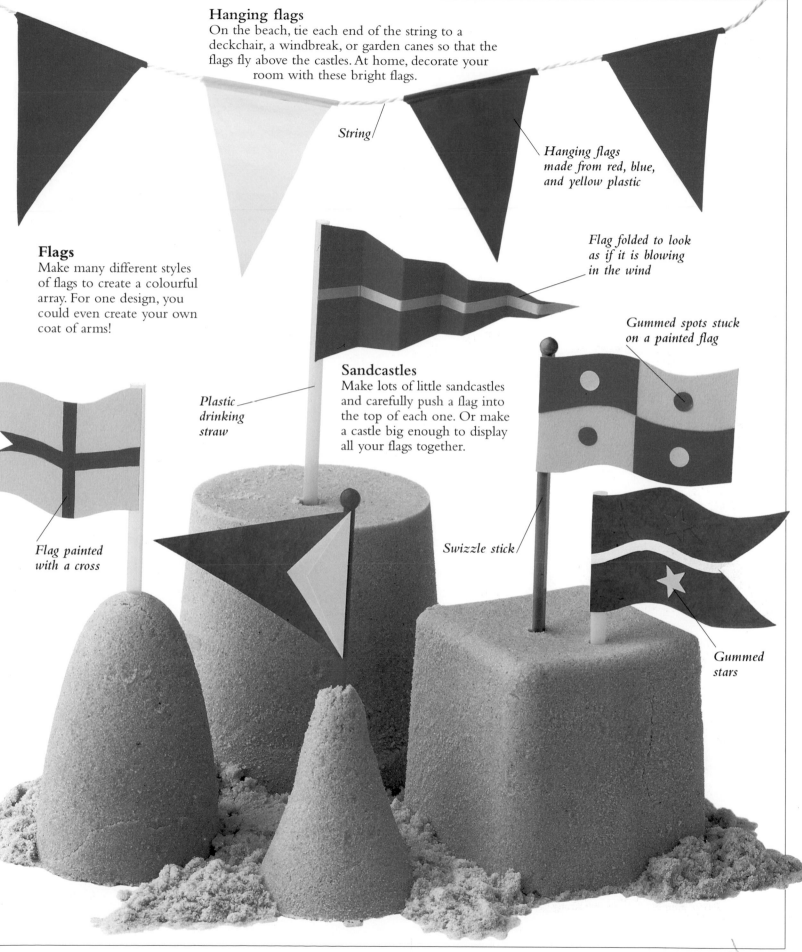

227

MARVELLOUS MOBILES

When it's raining outside and you are stuck indoors, why not make a new mobile for your room? Here you can find out how to make three brilliant mobiles from card or oven-hardening modelling clay using one simple method. Copy the themes we have shown here or create one of your own.

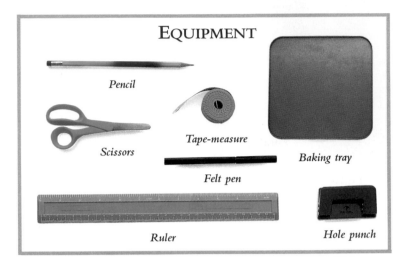

EQUIPMENT

Pencil

Scissors

Tape-measure

Baking tray

Felt pen

Ruler

Hole punch

You will need

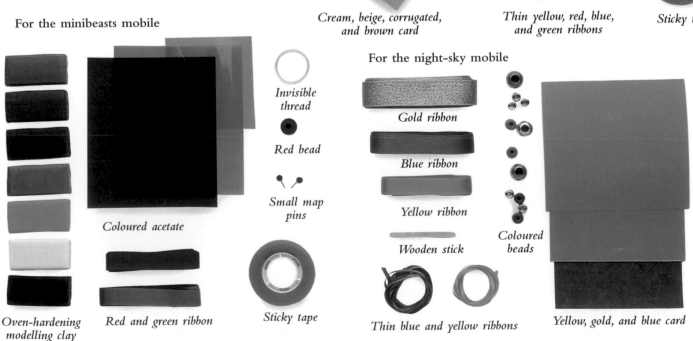

For each mobile

Strong glue

For the carousel mobile

*Embroidery hoop
20–22 cm in diameter*

*Cream, beige, corrugated,
and brown card*

Red bead

Tiny beads

Checked ribbons

*Thin yellow, red, blue,
and green ribbons*

Sticky tape

For the minibeasts mobile

*Invisible
thread*

Red bead

*Small map
pins*

Coloured acetate

*Oven-hardening
modelling clay*

Red and green ribbon

Sticky tape

For the night-sky mobile

Gold ribbon

Blue ribbon

Yellow ribbon

Wooden stick

*Coloured
beads*

Thin blue and yellow ribbons

Yellow, gold, and blue card

Night-sky mobile

1 Draw stars and moons on yellow, gold, and blue card and cut them out. For the centre of the mobile, draw and cut out a big quarter moon.

2 Punch a hole in each shape. Tie a thin ribbon through each hole and thread on a bead. Tie the moon to a wide ribbon 40 cm long.

3 Cover the embroidery hoop by wrapping blue and gold ribbon around it. Glue the ends of the ribbons in place to secure them.

Minibeasts mobile

4 Cut four ribbons 30 cm long. Glue one end of each ribbon to the hoop. Thread the other ends and the moon's ribbon through a big bead.

5 Hold the mobile up to check that it hangs straight. Tie on the other stars and moon, checking that the mobile is still hanging straight.

1 Knead the clay and roll it into balls. Shape characters and leaves with different coloured clay. Use the stick to help you model the minibeasts.

2 Put the minibeasts on a baking tray and harden them in the oven*. Allow to cool. For some insects, glue on coloured acetate wings.

3 Tie thread to each minibeast and check that it will hang straight. You may need to tie a thread to each end of the minibeast for balance.

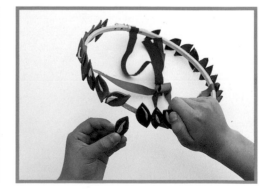

4 Tape ribbons to the hoop, as above. Glue the clay leaves around the hoop for decoration. Hang the mobile up and tie on the minibeasts.

*Ask an adult to help you harden the clay. Always follow the instructions on the packet carefully.

MERRY-GO-ROUND!
Carousel mobile

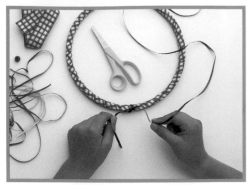

1 Wrap checked ribbon around the hoop to cover it. Cut eight thin ribbons 90 cm long. Tie each one to the hoop, leaving 45 cm on one side.

2 Draw eight horse shapes on card and cut them out. Glue on the checked-ribbon saddles and the thin, coloured-ribbon bridles and reins.

3 Thread the eight ribbons through a bead and check that the mobile hangs straight. Tape the other ends of the ribbons to the backs of the horses.

Displaying your mobile

Tie a loop in the ribbons above the bead and ask an adult to help you hang the mobile from the ceiling. Once it is up, you may have to adjust the position of some of the hanging objects so that the mobile balances well. For the best effect, hang the mobile where it will turn slowly in a breeze.

Fairground carousel
The finished mobile looks just like a fairground merry-go-round. For an added feeling of movement, trim the ribbons to different lengths and tape them to the back of the horses.

The eight pieces of ribbon tied to the bound hoop help balance the carousel.

Bead glued on as an eye

Bridles made of ribbon and beads

Ribbon taped to the back of the horse

Checked-ribbon saddles

Corrugated card

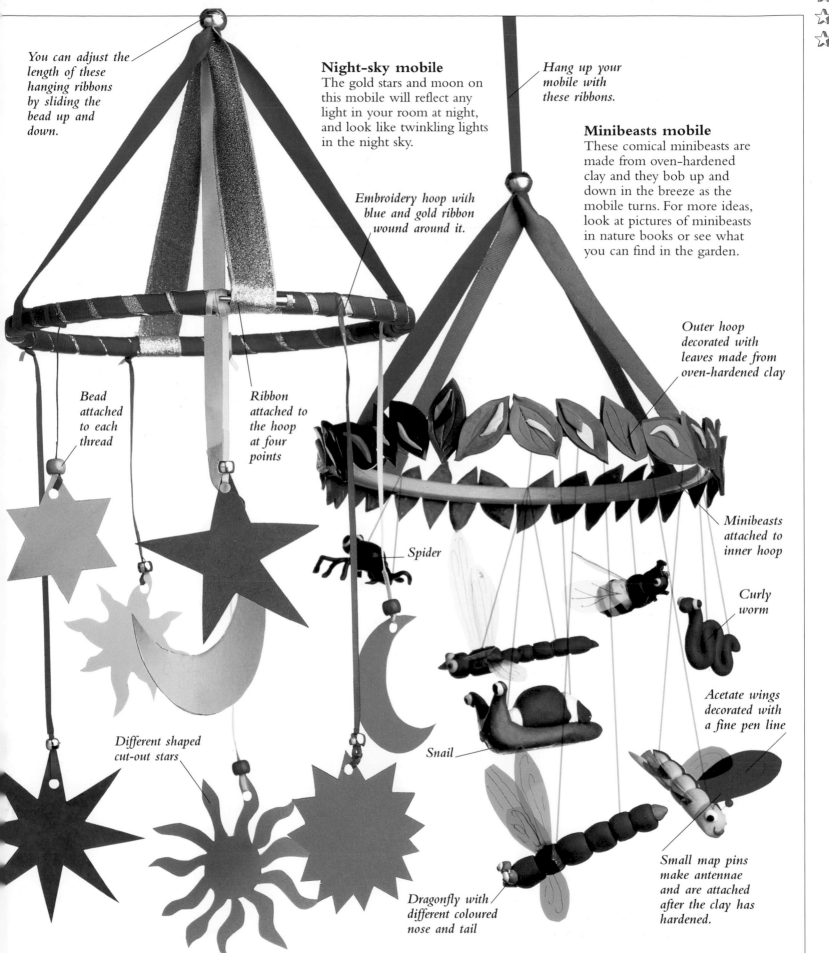

You can adjust the length of these hanging ribbons by sliding the bead up and down.

Night-sky mobile
The gold stars and moon on this mobile will reflect any light in your room at night, and look like twinkling lights in the night sky.

Hang up your mobile with these ribbons.

Minibeasts mobile
These comical minibeasts are made from oven-hardened clay and they bob up and down in the breeze as the mobile turns. For more ideas, look at pictures of minibeasts in nature books or see what you can find in the garden.

Embroidery hoop with blue and gold ribbon wound around it.

Outer hoop decorated with leaves made from oven-hardened clay

Bead attached to each thread

Ribbon attached to the hoop at four points

Minibeasts attached to inner hoop

Spider

Curly worm

Snail

Acetate wings decorated with a fine pen line

Different shaped cut-out stars

Dragonfly with different coloured nose and tail

Small map pins make antennae and are attached after the clay has hardened.

231

HANDY HINTS

This picture guide illustrates skills that you will find helpful for some of the projects in this book. If you want to practise your reef knots, use different coloured rope or string, as in the steps below.

Using a compass

1 Hold the compass steady in your hand and away from anything metal. Then wait until the coloured end of the needle stops moving.

2 Turn the compass around until the coloured end of the needle lines up with the symbol for North. You are now facing magnetic North.

Hammering in a nail

1 Using a ruler and pencil, make marks on the exact positions where you want the nails to go into the piece of wood.

2 Hold the nail about halfway down and position it on a pencil mark. Give it a firm tap with the hammer to drive it into the wood.

3 Remove your hand and, holding the hammer near the end, hit the nail squarely until its head lies on the surface of the wood.

Tying a reef knot

1 Hold the ends of two pieces of rope or string in each hand. Wrap the end of the green rope over then under the end of the yellow rope.

2 Now take the free end of the green rope and place it right over and then across the end of the yellow rope.

3 Finally, wrap the green rope right around the yellow rope and up through the hole in the middle. Then pull both ends of the rope tightly.

OUTDOOR CODE

Whatever you are doing outside, whether going for
a walk or arranging a nature expedition, plan your activities
sensibly and take care of the countryside and its wildlife.
Here are some important points to remember:

•

Always tell your parents or carers where
you are going and what you plan to do.

•

Before setting off, make sure you are wearing suitable clothes, have all
the equipment and food you need, and have change for a phone call home.

•

Do not drop litter. Take any rubbish home with you.

•

Keep to paths and fasten all gates behind you.

•

Always leave things as you found them. Do not damage any plants or trees.

•

When collecting things in the wild, only take what you need
and make sure you leave plenty of specimens behind.

•

Only pick wild flowers if there are plenty growing, and just
pick a few. Never pick rare plants or uproot any plant.

•

Never disturb nesting birds or take birds' eggs.

•

Be gentle with any creatures you catch. Study them
gently, make notes quickly, and then put them
back where you found them.

HANDY TIPS

This picture guide shows you all the useful craft and sewing skills that you need to make the projects in this book.

Drawing a circle

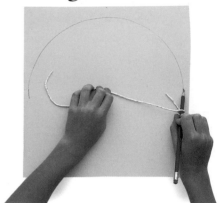

Tie a pencil to a piece of string. Hold the string where you want the centre of the circle to be. Move the pencil around it, keeping the string taut.

Scoring a fold

1 To make a sharp fold in card, you must score the fold-line first. Hold the ruler along the fold-line and run the tip of your scissors along the line.

2 Be careful not to cut right through the card! Gently smooth the fold down flat along the scored line. The card should fold over easily.

Drawing a square

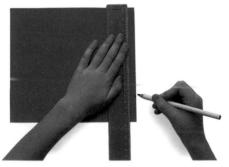

1 Starting from one corner of a piece of paper, measure along one edge and draw a dot. Then draw another dot the same distance along the other edge.

2 Imagine or draw a diagonal line between the two dots and fold the paper along it. Draw a dot at the folded corner of the paper, as shown.

3 Open out the paper and join the centre dot to the two dots at the edges of the paper. Cut along these two lines to make a perfect square.

Transferring a template

1 Trace the template from the outline on pages 236–237. Turn the tracing paper over and scribble all over the back of it, as shown.

2 Turn the tracing paper over and tape it on to a piece of card to hold it steady. Then carefully draw over the lines of the tracing.

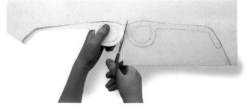

3 Remove the tracing paper. The tracing will have transferred on to the card below. Cut out the shape along the lines of the tracing.

Tracing-paper patterns

The templates for all the sewing projects are on pages 236–237. To make a pattern, trace the template you need on to a piece of tracing paper, and cut it out. Then follow steps 1 and 2 to cut out the fabric pieces. When cutting out two pieces from a pattern, fold the fabric in half, right sides together, with its pattern running straight up and down.

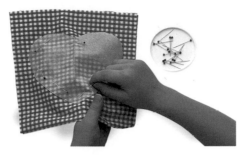

1 Pin the pattern piece to the fabric, making sure that the pattern is lying straight along the fabric pattern, as shown.

2 Cut around the edge of the pattern piece. Turn the fabric as you cut so that the scissors are always pointing away from you.

Trimming a seam

Trimming off the spare fabric around a seam makes the finished seam look neat. Cut halfway between the seam line and the edge, as shown.

Overstitch

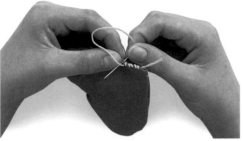

1 Fold in the edges of the fabric. Tie a knot in one end of the thread★, then push the needle through both folded edges from back to front.

2 Take the needle round to the back again and repeat the stitch until the seam is finished.

Running stitch

Tie a knot in the end of the thread★, and push the needle through both pieces of fabric then back through to the front, as shown in step 1. Then pull the thread and the needle out through the fabric (step 2). Repeat steps 1 and 2 until you have finished the seam.

Backstitch

Tie a knot in the thread★. Make the first stitch in the same way as the running stitch. Then put the needle through the hole at the end of the first stitch and up again a little way in front of the stitch you have just made, as shown in step 1. Repeat steps 1 and 2 until you have finished the seam.

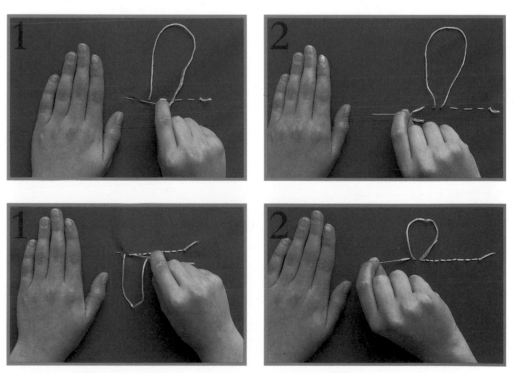

TEMPLATES

He are the templates for the soft toys on pages 22–23, the disguises on pages 118–119, and the puppets on page 200–201. You can find out how to make the templates and patterns on pages 234 and 235. Read the labels around the template you need before you start to make it.

Cutting line

Using a pattern
Ask an adult to help you line up the top and bottom of the pattern with the grain of the fabric before pinning them both together.

Top

Cutting line

Top

Top

Top

Fold line

Cutting line

Fold line

Bottom

White rabbit's ears
Make a tracing-paper pattern, as shown on page 235, and cut out two ears. Fold each ear in half along the dotted line and sew along the open sides, about 1 cm in from the cut edge.

Cutting line

Little cat
Make a tracing-paper pattern, as shown on page 235. Fold a piece of fabric in half, right sides together, and pin the pattern to the fabric so that the dotted line lies along the fold. Cut the fabric out and then sew the open sides together, about 1 cm in from the cut edge.

Fold line

Bottom

Finger-puppet template
Trace the pattern on to card
and cut it out, as shown on
page 234. Then look on page
200 for what to do next.

Cutting line

Cutting line

Top

**Dancing bear
or teddy**
Make a tracing-paper
pattern, as shown
on page 235. You
will need to cut out
two pieces of fabric
for each bear.

Bottom

Martha doll and white rabbit
Make a tracing-paper pattern, as shown
on page 235. You will need to cut out
two pieces of fabric for each doll or
rabbit. Sew around the open sides,
about 1 cm in from the cut edge.

Cutting line

Cutting line

Cutting line

Bottom

Eye patch
Trace the pattern on to
card and cut it out, as
shown on page 234.
Then turn to page 118 to
find out what to do next.

Top

Soft heart
Make a tracing-
paper pattern, as
shown on page
235. Cut out two
pieces of fabric
for each heart.

Cutting line

Glasses template
Make a card template with wings for the
movie-star shades or without the wings
for the disguise, as shown on page 234.

INDEX

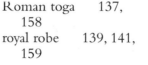

Dorling DK Kindersley

LONDON, NEW YORK, SYDNEY, DELHI, PARIS,
MUNICH, AND JOHANNESBURG

Managing Editor Jane Yorke
Managing Art Editors Chris Scollen and Gillian Allan
Editors Carey Combe, Helen Drew, Victoria Edgley, and Hannah Wilson
Designers Jane Bull, Adrienne Hutchinson, Joanna Malivoire, Katie Poyner, Dean Price, and Cheryl Telfer
Production Josie Alabaster, Melanie Dowland, and Katy Holmes
Photographers Andy Crawford, Dave King, and Steve Gorton
Home Economist Jane Suthering

First published in Great Britain in 2000 by
Dorling Kindersley Limited
9 Henrietta Street
Covent Garden, London WC2E 8PS

2 4 6 8 10 9 7 5 3 1

A CIP catalogue record for this book
is available from the British Library.

ISBN: 0-7513-1363-7

Colour reproduction by Colourscan, Singapore
Printed and bound by LREX, China

Dorling Kindersley would like to thank Jonathan Buckley, Sarah Cowley, Jackie Gooden, John Hutchinson,
Jeannette Morton, Emma Patmore, Anne-Marie Ryan, and Lissa Martin from World's End Nurseries.

Dorling Kindersley would also like to thank the following models: Ellisha Akhtar, Maria Beckworth,
Sarah Bennett, Thomas Brightman, Montana Burrett-Manning, Micheal Busby, Olivia Busby, Gina Caffrey, Samantha Cobb,
Holly Cowgill, Jay Davis, Candy Day, Scott Dennis, Duran Earle, Kelly Gomez, Collette Haydon, Lorna Holmes, Emma Judson,
Laurence King, Sam King, Connie Kirkby, Taskin Kuyucuoglu, Tolga Kuyucuoglu, Scott Lamb, Johnathan Lawrence, Gemma Loke,
Johnathan McInyre, Kim Ng, Lian Ng, Jade Ogugua, Natasha Payne, Sam Priddy, Tebedge Ricketts, Tim Shaw, Darren Singh,
Selena Singh, Danielle Smith, Kirsty Thomas, Phoebe Thoms, Natasha Trinnamen, Chloe Whitmarsh, and Elizabeth Workman

Picture credits: The Image Bank/Sumo: 211cl, 213tl. Tony Stone Images: 177tr, 185tr, Keren Su 161crb, Glen Allison 173crb, S&N Geary 194cb,
Renee Lynn 163cr, Herb Schmitz 177br. Planet Earth Pictures: 198bl, 169cr. Rex Features: 191cr. Hutchison: 187tr, 165br, S. Errington 164br.
Panos Pictures:162tl. Robert Harding Picture Library: 183crb. Additional photography: Dave King 172tl, British Museum C Graham/N Nicholls 179cl,
B&A Kindersley 189br, Colin Keates 167br, Jerry Young 171br, Steve Shott 170tl, Susanna Price 197br.

see our complete
catalogue at
www.dk.com